S0-BBM-717

PERU FROM THE AIR

Ships of the guano fleet at anchor in Callao Bay with the irrigated fields of the delta of the Rimac River in the background. (For photographs of the guano islands see Figs. 44, 101, and 102. See also note on the guano industry, page 157.)

AMERICAN GEOGRAPHICAL SOCIETY
SPECIAL PUBLICATION NO. 12

PERU FROM THE AIR

BY

LIEUTENANT GEORGE R. JOHNSON
Commanding Officer, 119th Photographic Section, 44th Division Aviation, New Jersey National Guard
Former Chief Photographer, Peruvian Naval Air Service

WITH TEXT AND NOTES BY

RAYE R. PLATT
Head, Department of Hispanic American Research
American Geographical Society

AMERICAN GEOGRAPHICAL SOCIETY
BROADWAY AT 156TH STREET
NEW YORK
1930

COMMONWEALTH PRESS WORCESTER, MASS.

CONTENTS

COAST RANGES AND HIGH PAMPAS

OLD VOLCANOES OF THE WESTERN ANDES

EASTERN VALLEYS AND LOWLANDS

MAPS AND SKETCHES IN THE INTRODUCTION AND NOTES

PREFACE

The aerial photographs of Peru presented in this volume were selected from a large collection taken by Lieutenant George R. Johnson, a fellow of the American Geographical Society, in his official capacity as Chief Photographer of the Peruvian Naval Air Service and Instructor in Aerial Photography at the Naval Air Base at Ancón from June 15, 1928, to January 1, 1930. Three groups of photographs, giving a representative cross section of the topography of Peru and the life of its people, have been selected: (1) Photographs of characteristic features of the coastal region—its irrigated valleys and their ports, its desert plains and barren mountains, its coastal terraces and the high coastal hills that form much of the border of the land; (2) a series of photographs taken in a flight from the port of Mollendo across the Coast Range and the high desert pampas that lie between it and the Andes to Arequipa, and thence up through the snow-capped volcanic peaks that crown the western margin of the plateau of the Andes in the vicinity of Arequipa to the deep gorge of the Colca River with its terraced valley floor, its close-set villages, and its pasture lands high up on the mature, waste-cloaked surface of the plateau summit; and (3) a series of photographs of the Chanchamayo Valley, best known of the eastern valleys of the Peruvian Andes, and of scenes along the Ucayali River and its tributaries in the Amazon lowland.

Lieutenant Johnson wishes to express his thanks to Commander H. B. Grow, U. S. Naval Reserve, Inspector-General of Aviation of Peru, under whose direction the majority of the photographs were made, to Commander B. Wyatt, U. S. Navy, Commanding Officer of the Peruvian Naval Air Base at Ancón, to Lieutenant Alvarino, Peruvian Naval Air Service, Commanding Officer at the Naval Air Base at San Ramón, and to the pilots who flew the planes from which the photographs were taken—Lieutenant Lloyd Moore, U. S. Navy, Chief Instructor at the Ancón Naval Air Base, Lieutenant C. K. Travis, U. S. Army Reserve Corps, Chief Instructor of the Peruvian Army Air Corps, and Ensign Pedro Greva, Peruvian Naval Air Service, who piloted the official planes, and Henry Elliot and Captain H. R. Harris, of the Pan American-Grace Airways, who piloted the commercial planes from which a number of the photographs were taken.

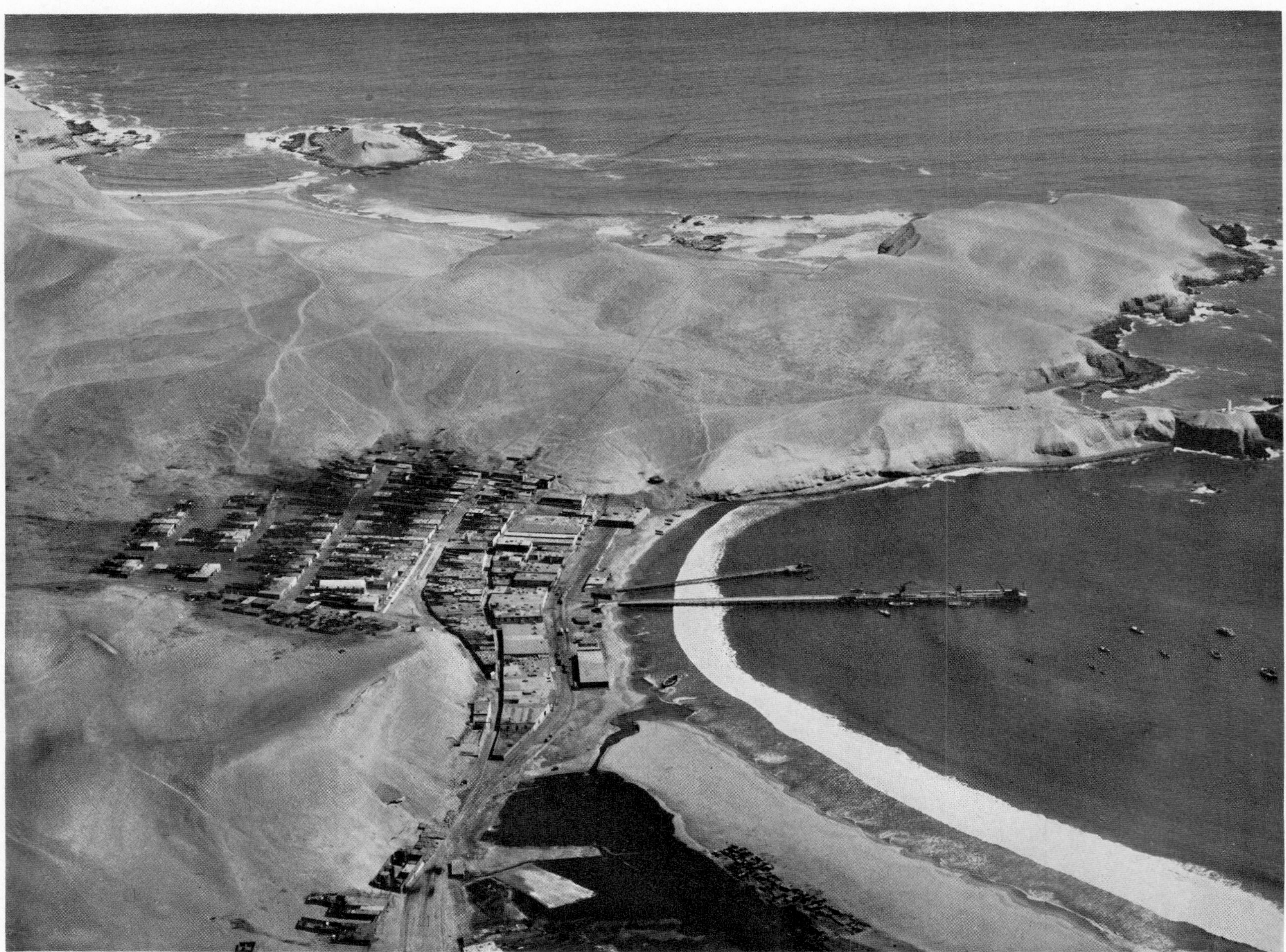

Fig. 1—The port of Supé, shipping and receiving port for the irrigated sugar and cotton plantations of the Supé, Pativilca, and Fortaleza valleys (see map, Fig. 2). In a cove on the sheltered, northern side of a broad headland (Tomás Point) there is comparatively quiet water. There piers have been built, equipped with cranes for loading and unloading and railway tracks for transferring cargo to and from the shore. A railway leading from the piers toward the foreground at the left of the lagoon connects them with the valleys which they serve. Even in this cove the swell is so heavy that ships anchor well offshore and load and unload by means of the launches shown tied at the piers and anchored near by.

THE PERUVIAN LANDSCAPE

THE COASTAL VALLEYS AND THEIR PORTS

ON the opposite page is an aerial photograph of the port of Supé, on the coast of Peru. It is one of the simplest of ports—headland and piers and, at the end of the piers, a settlement of stevedores and boatmen set down in regular pattern on the sand. The headland shelters a cove of quiet water. If there were no headland there could be no pier; and if there were no pier there would be no settlement. All other features which one may recognize in the photograph—beach and sand-covered hills with their network of local trails, the railway in the foreground, the pattern of the village streets, the lighthouse on the point at the entrance to the harbor—though interesting in themselves, are subordinate to the primary need that has determined the location of the port—relatively quiet water in which steamers, anchored well offshore where they are safe from the surf, can load and unload cargoes.

One should not be misled by the small size of this port. Thirty thousand acres of irrigated land in the near-by valleys of the Supé, Pativilca, and Fortaleza rivers export their crops—sugar and cotton, mostly—through it, and through it import a great variety of manufactured wares. Back of the hills that surround its desolate streets and squalid houses are fields of growing crops on the rich, alluvial soil of river deltas, where men keep a network of irrigation ditches in careful repair, jealously enforce the ancient laws that regulate the distribution of water to them, and husband every precious drop of it that it may do its full share in moistening the rainless land. The piers express the successful application of their ingenuity and labor.

The settlement of stevedores and boatmen now numbers about five hundred persons. It must have been much smaller when the shorter, wooden pier served the port. It must have known sudden growth when the new pier of steel and concrete was constructed. If new lands are brought under irrigation in the near-by valleys, new rows of houses of wattle and mud plaster will be erected at the port. If, even for a season, there is a decrease in the products of the valley, there will be stevedores and boatmen who must seek their livelihood elsewhere, and houses at the port will be abandoned. For this is a settlement with but a single motive—to serve the piers.

In the valleys behind the hills are thriving towns in the midst of fertile fields, with a variety of activities and interests, manufacturing of a simple sort, barter and trade. Here at the port, life is only a reflection of activity on the piers. Here is neither market place nor distributing center. Exports and imports barely pause here on their way to and from the ships at anchor in the bay. The hills that surround the settlement contribute not a single item to its daily needs. There is not even the smallest of garden plots, not a tree to relieve the glare of the sand. Even the church shows only a low, white roof without the usual bell tower, as though it, too, had been erected to serve only the barest of necessities.

Here, in fact, are recorded in a single photograph, in such simple form as to be almost diagrammatic, the essential features that characterize the ports of Peru. In this volume many of these ports are shown as they appear from the air. They will be seen to differ greatly in certain details—in size, in the topographic character of their surroundings, and in various manifestations of communal life. But, with few exceptions, they have been established where a bit of headland or a group of islands provides a stretch of relatively quiet water in which a pier can be built and ships at anchor can be afforded some measure of protection. In all of them settlement, roads, and railways exist only as functions of the pier.

Only from the air could one obtain such a comprehensive

view of even so simple a scene as this little port of Supé. From the sea it is only a line of low, flat-roofed buildings against a background of barren hills. On the ground minor details obscure its simple, essential features. From an airplane or, better still, in an aerial photograph (for the camera catches and records much that the eye cannot grasp in the rapid flight of the plane) one sees the whole scene spread out in a single, unhindered panorama in which the broader features and relationships are lifted clear and unmistakable from the details that conceal them on the ground.

There are thirty of these ports on the coast of Peru. A few—Salaverry, Chimbote, Callao, and Mollendo—are ports not only for coastal valleys but for mining districts in the Andes as well. The majority, however, have but a single function—to connect a near-by irrigated valley or group of valleys with the sea. Valley, railway or road, and port together form a complete and independent economic unit. There is no continuous railway running from valley to valley across the desert to connect them with a common center of distribution and supply. Their great transportation trunk line is the sea.

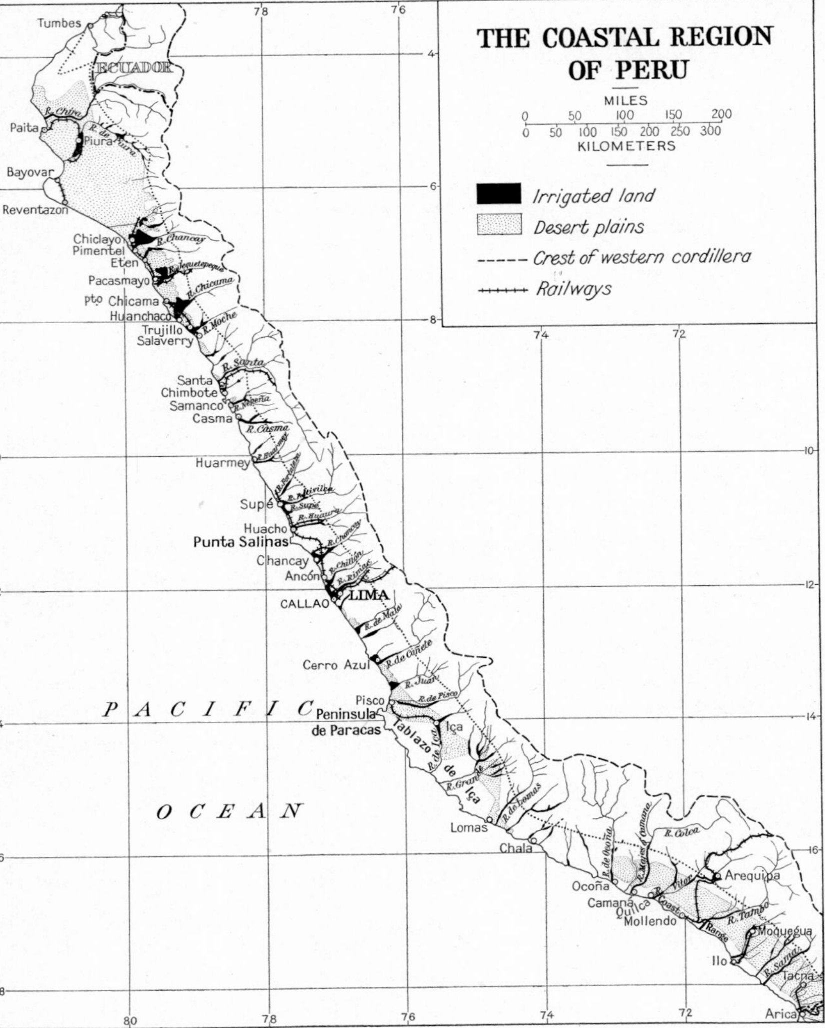

FIG. 2—Map showing the irrigated coastal valleys of Peru and their ports. The dotted line is the approximate boundary between the mountain zone of annual rains and the coastal zone with rains only at intervals of several years.

To it each seeks an outlet by the shortest possible route to the nearest point where a pier can be built. Each sends its products to foreign markets and imports its manufactured supplies from abroad.

A third of the people of Peru live in these irrigated valleys and their ports. Yet, seen on a map of the coastal region (Fig. 2) they seem insignificant as compared with the wide stretches of desert that surround them and isolate them from each other. In a flight by airplane along the coast they are only incidents of the journey—occasional oases in the desert, ribbons of green along the banks of widely separated rivers, broader patches of green on alluvial fans and deltas—pleasant and restful to the eyes after the glare of the desert but soon passed. The larger of them, like the Rimac delta and the famous group of valleys in the Department of Lambayeque, are impressive—dotted with haciendas and towns, criss-crossed by roads and railways. But even these are, at the most, only a few hundred square miles in extent. All the valleys together occupy not more than three per cent of the whole coastal region between the crests of the western border of the Andes and the sea. Yet they contain a sixth of the 4,000,000

Fig. 3—A section of a mosaic made from photographs taken in an aerial survey of the Chillón Valley (see map, Fig. 4). In a valley bordered by barren spurs from the Andes the Chillón River has built a narrow flood plain. The river has its source in the zone of snow and rain in the Andes, and has, as a result, built its flood plain so much more rapidly than the infrequent rains of the coastal region have been able to wear away the spurs or build up the alluvial fans between them that the waste from these spurs and fans has had no important effect on the character of the border of the plain. Their junction with it is along a remarkably sharp line. Along this line desert and well watered plain meet. The river is shallow, its braided channel filled with bars and islands. In the thick growth of trees at the base of the spur in the center of the mosaic and in the patterns of light and dark soil which show even in the cultivated fields are the marks of former channels occupied by the river. Now a close planting of trees and shrubs has been made along its outermost bank in an attempt to hold it to its present bed. All parts of the area occupied by the flood plain of the river are irrigated and tilled except for a few erosion remnants—in the photograph, small gray spots, apparently only a few feet above the level of the irrigated fields.

acres estimated to be under cultivation in the whole of Peru, and such is their fertility and productiveness that the value of their annual crop is nearly equal to that of all the other agricultural areas of the country combined, while the exports of sugar and cotton alone from them are now about equal in value to the country's total exports of copper, silver, and petroleum.

THE VALLEYS OF THE RIMAC AND CHILLON RIVERS

The mosaic (Fig. 3) shows a section of one of these valleys—the upper valley of the Chillón River—as it appears to an observer looking vertically down upon it from the air. Here are to be seen, as on a living map, the essential elements of the coastal valleys of Peru. A river, flowing across the desert in a shallow, many-channeled bed, has built a flood plain of fertile alluvial soil and furnishes water for its irrigation. As far as irrigation canals can carry water from the river, there are fields of growing crops, groups of hacienda buildings, isolated laborers' huts, and roads. Wherever water from the river cannot reach is desert.

Beyond the foothills of the Andes the Chillón Valley joins the lower flood plain of the Rimac River—a broad delta plain, as shown on the map (Fig. 4) and in the oblique aerial photographs (Figs. 5, 6, and 7), irrigated and tilled to the very shore line, set with towns and villages, served by a network of roads and railways. There, as in the narrow Chillón Valley, all life depends upon the river. As far as the varitinted patchwork of fields extends there can be seen the shining threads of irrigation ditches. Wherever there are towns the river supplies the water and sanitation systems and turns the hydro-electric generators which furnish current for lighting systems and for street and interurban railways.

Skilled engineers seek constantly for new means to augment the flow of the river. Dams and reservoirs hoard the excess water of flood time against the seasons of drought. Walls are built and trees planted to hold the river to its bed. The laws governing the maintenance of the canals and the conservation and distribution of water outweigh all others in their importance in the eyes of the people of the valley. For on the supply of water furnished by the river depends the acreage that can be planted, the type of crops

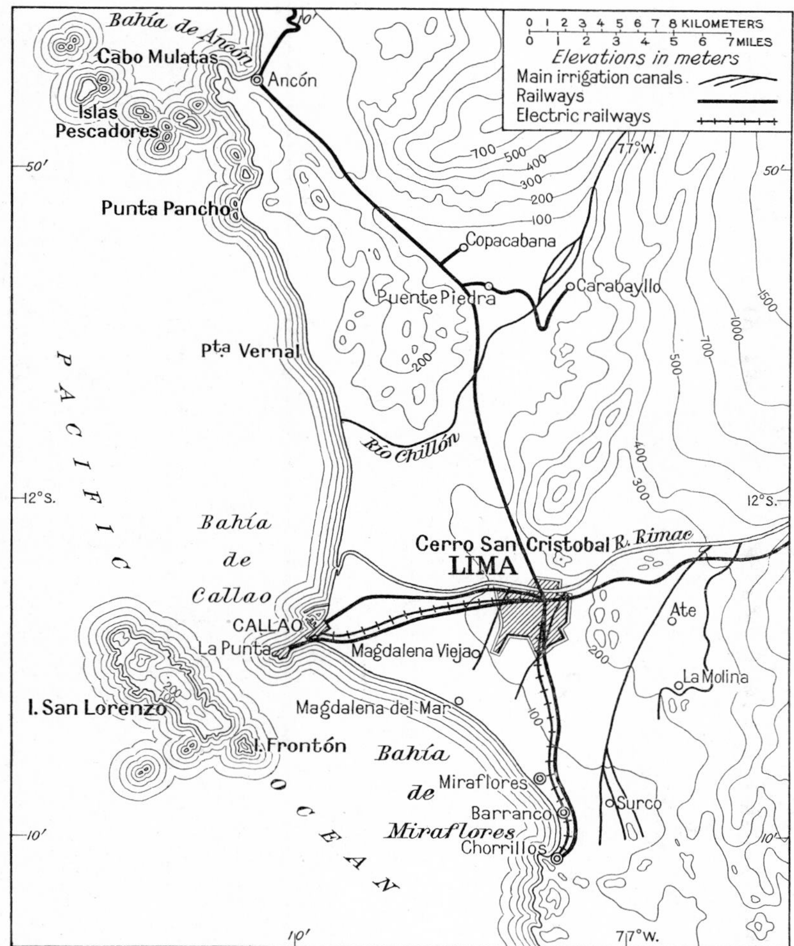

FIG. 4—Map of the Rimac and Chillón valleys. Beyond the foothills the two valleys unite to form a broad delta plain which extends down to the shore. The railway leading out of the map at the right is the Central Railway of Peru.

FIG. 5—The lower Chillón Valley. The railway that crosses the irrigated fields is the line from Lima to Ancón, and the town in the center of the photograph is Puente Piedra (see Fig. 4). The sharp line at which the flood plain meets the edge of the spurs that border it is especially striking in this photograph. Isolated outliers of these spurs stand like islands in the midst of the irrigated fields. Water from the irrigation canals cannot reach them. Waste from the spurs and outliers accumulates so slowly under the infrequent rains of the coastal region as compared with the upbuilding of the flood plain that it seems to have no marked effect on the level of the flood plain even at its edge.

FIG. 6—A view across the city of Lima and a section of the Rimac Valley from above the foothills bordering the valley on the north, with the seaside suburbs of Barranco and Chorrillos faintly visible in the upper right corner.

FIG. 7—South of Lima the Rimac Valley is a level, unbroken stretch of irrigated fields reaching down to the sea. The foothills of the Andes rise abruptly from it. The main irrigation canals from the river follow the junction line of plain and foothills, and the distributing canals from them divide again and again until every field is bordered by flowing water. (See also Figs. 82 to 99.)

that can be brought to maturity, the location and size of towns, the character and number of roads and railways. If there were no river, where now are luxuriant fields of sugar cane and cotton, market gardens, and alfalfa meadows, there would be only desert as arid and lifeless as the hills that border them. There would be no towns, no roads or railways. There might even be no port, for the mining centers in the Andes, which now export their products and import their supplies through the port of Callao by way of the Central Railway along the Rimac Valley, might well have chosen an outlet to the sea by a route less difficult of construction and maintenance had it not been politic, at a time when mining was the chief industry of the country, to connect its richest mines with its capital and its chief port.

LOCATION AND CHARACTER OF THE COASTAL VALLEYS

In their essential features the coastal valleys are alike. All owe their existence to rivers, fed by melting snows and seasonal rains in the Andes, which flow across the desert, building flood plains and deltas and furnishing water for their irrigation. The valleys differ greatly, however, not only in size and in the amount of water available for irrigation but also in the topographic character of their settings and in their position with respect to the sea. North of Salaverry the foothills of the Andes stand far back from the coast, and the delta plains at the mouths of the rivers have been built up on broad desert pampas, so-called, which lie open to the sea. From Salaverry to Cerro Azul south of Lima, spurs from the Andes themselves reach down to the shore, and the only irrigable land is the flood plains and deltas built up by the rivers between the spurs. South of Cerro Azul the pampas begin again, but they are hidden from the sea by a broken line of hills which, from the Ocoña River to Point Paracas, forms the northerly extension of the coast ranges. Southward from the Ocoña River to the Chilean border the pampas form a plateau several thousand feet high separated from the sea by the well-defined system of the true coast ranges. There the irrigated land is on the narrow floors of deep transverse gorges cut by rivers on their way from the Andes to the sea and on terraces built on alluvial fans tributary to the main valleys.

In the narrow valleys of the southern part of the coastal region the crops are grown chiefly to supply food to the mining districts of near-by sections of the plateau and are consequently much diversified—barley and potatoes on the higher levels; alfalfa, wheat, and corn farther down; grapes, olives, and some sugar cane and cotton on the lower valley floor. Elsewhere crops for export are the chief consideration to the almost complete exclusion, in many of the valleys, of food crops for local consumption. The valleys of the Grande, Içа, and Pisco rivers are devoted almost exclusively to the cultivation of cotton and grapes, from the latter of which the famous *pisco* brandy is made. From there northward the chief crops are sugar and cotton for export and rice for local consumption. On the Rimac delta there are alfalfa meadows and market gardens, but they are far outweighed by the acreage in cotton and cane and supply only a part of the needs of the populous towns of the delta. Outside the valleys cultivation is limited to spots along the base of the seaward front of the coast ranges where, here and there, are small olive groves, a vegetable garden, or a narrow alfalfa meadow irrigated by tiny streams or springs that derive their water from the zone of clouds and fogs on the upper slopes of the ranges. The upper slopes of the coast ranges also furnish sparse pasturage for a short period of the year.

From the sea one gets only rare glimpses of these valleys. High, dune-covered coastal terraces, barren coast ranges, or massive spurs of the Andes themselves, their seaward slopes cut to steep cliffs by the steady pounding of the surf, are all that the camera has caught even from the air in many of the photographs of the coast presented in this volume. In most of the photographs they are the predomi-

FIG. 8—The irrigated cane and cotton fields of the valley of the Huaura River come down to the shore at the port of Huacho, and the river carries water to the sea most of the year. Its main channel, thickly lined with trees and shrubs, can be seen in the center of the photograph, and the outlets of several irrigation canals from it enter the sea beneath the road that follows the shore. This is the *puerto* of Huacho. The main town, the *pueblo* (the most important town between Lima and Trujillo, with a population of about 5000), is close to the sea about a mile north of this little cove where the *puerto* has been built. *Pueblo* and *puerto* are connected by rail with Lima.

nating features. They form the greater part of the border of the land and shut off all view from the sea except for an occasional glimpse of the lofty wall of the Andes thrusting its head into the clouds or revealing here and there the dim outlines of a snow-capped peak. Even where the coastal terraces are low there is usually to be seen only a strip of sun-baked desert landscape broken by irregular foothills that merge in the distance with the outer spurs of the Andes. Most of the rivers, except in time of flood, end before they reach the sea, their waters drawn off in irrigation canals or exhausted by evaporation.

Even from the air such views as the photograph of the port of Huacho (Fig. 8), with irrigated fields crowding the settlement at the pier to the very edge of the terrace and pushing it up on the slopes of the hills where water from irrigation ditches cannot reach, are as rare as they are charming. At most of the ports the background is, as at the port of Supé, bare hills and desert sand with only the pier and the busy coming and going of ships to hint of what lies beyond. Occasionally, as at Pimentel or off the low coast opposite Trujillo and Moche, one sees, back of a narrow strip of coastal desert, a wide expanse of irrigated fields stretching away toward the mountains. At Callao the irrigated fields of the Rimac delta border the shore. But these are all only occasional breaks in the rugged, sun-scorched, desert landscape.

FOG AND MIST ON A DESERT COAST

One must wonder to see a photograph like Figure 9 of a coast that has been described as desert. But fog like this is of frequent occurrence on the coast of Peru. To aviators who fly the regular routes along the coast it is no uncommon experience to have the sea and land hidden from them by a blanket of fog while the hot rays of the tropical sun beat down upon them from a clear sky. There is, perhaps, no more graphic description of the phenomenon than that contained in Samuel Purchas' translation from the writings of José de Acosta, a Jesuit who lived in Peru in the latter part of the sixteenth century: "Comming from the Mountaines to the Vallies, they doe usually see as it were two Heavens, one cleere and bright above, and the other obscure, and as it were a gray vaile spread underneath, which covers all the Coast."[1]

It is to the relatively low temperature of the Humboldt Current, which follows the shore of Peru as far north as Point Pariña, that this fog is due. It is on account of the contrast between the temperature of the current and that of the adjacent desert that rain seldom falls in any effective quantities in the coastal belt, however much of promise there may be in frequent menacing clouds. The current has a mean temperature 20° F. lower than the theoretical values for the surface of the ocean in the latitude of the coast of Peru. Onshore winds off warmer water beyond the current are cooled in crossing its cold waters. Fog banks, therefore, form over it and are carried over the land. For months during the winter season the sky as seen from the ground is overcast a large part of the time. Yet so warm is the land that rain rarely falls except on the upper slopes of the coastal hills and the coast ranges, where there is sufficient precipitation to support a sparse growth of drought-resisting plants and shrubs. Mists, known locally as *garuas*, are frequent even where the coast is low, and there may be occasional dashes of rain; but neither fog nor *garua* has any marked effect on the parched surface of the land. When the fog has lifted the ground is almost as dry as before.[2]

[1] Samuel Purchas: Hakluytus Posthumus, or Purchas His Pilgrimes, Contayning a History of the World in Sea Voyages and Lande Travells by Englishmen and others (20 vols., Glasgow and New York, 1905–1907), Vol. 15, p. 56.

[2] For a report on recent studies of the salinity and temperatures of the Humboldt Current see H. U. Sverdrup: Some Oceanographic Results of the *Carnegie's* Work in the Pacific—the Peruvian Current, *Trans. Amer. Geophys. Union, Tenth Annual Meeting, April 25 and 26, 1929,* [*and*] *Eleventh Annual Meeting, May 1 and 2, 1930,* National Research Council, Washington, D. C., pp. 257–264.

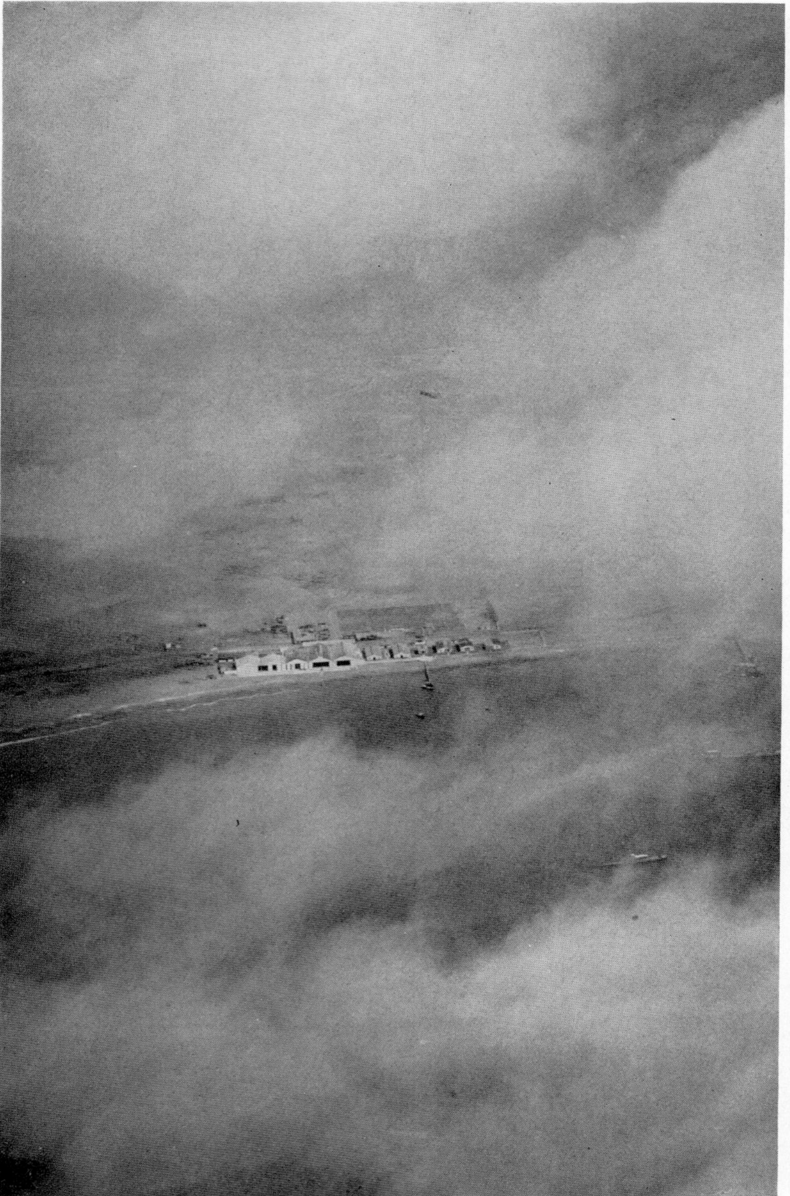

Fig. 9—Banks of fog drifting in from the sea at Ancón.

Fig. 10—The coastal desert at Ancón after the fog has lifted—as dry and barren as before.

THE COASTAL VALLEYS FROM THE GROUND AND FROM THE AIR

To the traveler by land these irrigated valleys, whether he approach them across the desert or down from the bleak cordilleras of the Andes, seem the height of scenic beauty. They are like sunken gardens, their fields and terraces all shades of green from the dull gray-green of algarrobo and olive trees to the bright green of freshly-watered alfalfa and the delicate tints of young cane. Against the background of yellow-brown hills and the white or yellow of drifting sand, their colors are intensified beyond imagination. On the border of the Andes the streams are deeply entrenched, often to depths of two thousand to four thousand feet, with walls that drop in places five hundred feet or more in sheer descents from one level to another. In places the cultivated fields are mere ribbons of green bordering a waste-strewn stream bed with the cliffs of the canyon close on either side. In places the whole valley may be terraced and cultivated from wall to wall with the stream winding in a narrow channel deeply cut in the valley floor and the threads of irrigation ditches leading down from terrace to terrace from sources far up the valley. Beyond the foothills of the Andes the flood plains widen; the groups of hacienda buildings stand closer together; towns appear; trails and roads form an ever closer network; until, finally, the streams finger out in numerous channels over broad delta plains, and except for the few that carry water to the sea throughout the year, disappear, leaving a strip of waterless desert between the deltas and the sea.

At best, however, the traveler by land sees these valleys only bit by bit, and his conception of them can be but a sort of mental mosaic. It is only from the air that one can see the whole entrancing panorama. There one has frequently, in a single view, the life of the valley complete. On the one hand may be seen the cordillera whose snows and rains feed the river that makes possible the green carpet of fields, the haciendas and towns, the sugar, rice, and cotton mills, the roads and railways spread out on all sides beneath the plane; and, on the other hand, if the day is clear, the little port with ships riding at anchor while they load the products of the valley or unload the manufactured articles sent back by the world in exchange.

PRE-COLONIAL AGRICULTURE IN THE COASTAL VALLEYS

Scarcely less impressive from the air than the works of the present-day occupants of the coastal valleys are the relics of the Inca and pre-Inca civilizations. The ruins of their cities, fortresses, and burial places dot the landscape throughout the coastal region. On the ground the crumbling remains of their adobe walls blend so well with the color of the earth that they are frequently passed unnoticed. From the air, where every shadow, every change of color catches the eye, their outlines are often the most striking features of the landscape. Chan-Chan (Figs. 11 and 12), near Trujillo in the Moche Valley, the capital of the kingdom of the Great Chimú whom the Incas subjugated shortly before the Spanish conquest of their own empire, is the largest of these and one of the most interesting. It covers about eleven square miles and may have had, at one time, a population of as many as 200,000 people. Its walls have crumbled, its gardens are drifted with sand, its irrigation ditches are empty; but, from the air, the pattern of the city, its houses and temples, its streets and the roads that entered it from across the plain, its irrigation system, and even the outlines of its cultivated fields are as clear as on a carefully plotted map.

The conquerors found these valleys well populated—much more densely populated than at present, many

Fig. 11—The largest of the so-called "palaces" of Chan-Chan—large blocks enclosed by massive walls and containing courts, streets, dwellings, and reservoirs for water. This structure is 1600 feet long by 1100 feet wide at its widest part. The rectangular, walled enclosure in the lower corner of the main block contains a structure made up of cell-like openings which is believed to have been a prison. The large excavation in the center of the block was probably a reservoir, while that in the foreground outside the wall is believed to be a sunken garden, made by digging down to a layer of earth moist enough to support vegetation. Remains of these sunken gardens are found in many places along the coast of Peru.

FIG. 12—The second in size of the "palaces" of Chan-Chan and like the larger in many respects. It contains, however, no reservoir; though there is a large one just outside the walls in the foreground of the photograph. In both of these photographs the walls of other lesser structures, the outline of the streets, and the areas originally in fields and gardens are clearly visible. (For a recent discussion of the ruins of Chan-Chan and an account of the pre-Incaic people of the Chimú Valley, see article entitled "Chan-Chan: The Capital of the Great Chimú," in the *Geographical Review*, January, 1927, by Major Otto Holstein, long a resident of Trujillo and an authority on the antiquities of the Chimú Valley.)

think—by an agricultural people living in contented assurance of a comfortable livelihood under a benevolent, though despotic, government which arranged for them and forced them to accept the whole plan of their daily lives from birth to death and provided for them highly efficient systems of irrigation and a well considered plan of land tenure, water rights, and crop rotation. Long before the coming of the Spaniards the valleys had been brought to a state of production that modern engineering skill and agricultural methods must still go far to restore. Great aqueducts had been built to bring water from distant sources, dams to conserve it and control its distribution, reservoirs to assure a full supply even during the seasons of drought at the sources of the rivers.

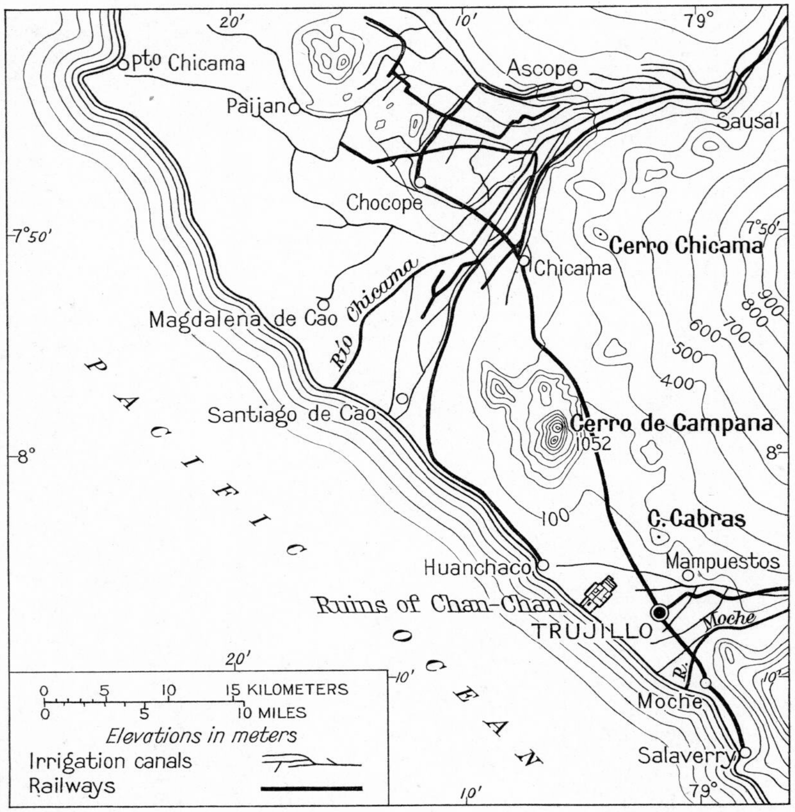

Fig. 13—Map of the Chicama and Moche valleys showing the location of the ruins of Chan-Chan, close to Trujillo.

Parts of these irrigation systems are still in use. But the majority were allowed to fall in ruin while the Spaniards turned their attention to exploiting the mineral resources of the country and impressed the farmers of the coast to work the mines of the plateau. The lands to which they had furnished an abundance of water returned to desert and have been even now only partially reclaimed. In many of the valleys there is still less water available for irrigation and less land cultivated than when the Spaniards took possession of them. Moreover, under the Inca system, the whole agricultural population was made up of small farmers to each of whom was assigned exactly the amount of land shown by experience to be sufficient for his own needs and for the required tribute to the treasury of his rulers and the temples of his gods. To each man was assured the amount of water necessary for the irrigation of his plot of land. Today the greater part of the valleys is in large estates, the titles of which date back to the early days of the Spanish occupation, with such land as is in small holdings located on their borders where the soil is poorest and where the water available for irrigation is only that left over from the needs of the large estates. In fact on many of the large estates there is much idle land and much that has only enough water for seasonal irrigation.

MODERN IRRIGATION PROJECTS IN THE COASTAL VALLEYS

But Peru is deeply concerned now with the possibility of further irrigation in the coastal valleys. Plans for increasing the supply of water for irrigation in them constituted one of the major interests of the Leguia administration. Good progress was made on many irrigation projects, partly by the Federal Government and partly by private enterprise with government aid and advice, which, if completed, will bring under irrigation a total of a million acres of new land in twenty valleys. In the Cañete Valley, eighty miles south of Lima, the Irrigation Commission of the Government has already irrigated and colonized 20,000 acres of new land. In many other valleys the supply of water has been increased and the means of distributing it improved. That the entire 20,000 acres of new land in the Cañete Valley was sold in one day, mostly in small lots, is evidence of the demand for land in the coastal region.

The most important project now under way is in the Department of Lambayeque (see map, Fig. 14), where are grouped the largest and richest of the coastal valleys, with, when the work began in 1924, a perennial water supply for only 62,000 acres and a seasonal supply for an additional 125,000 acres. When the work is completed a full perennial supply of water will be provided for 355,000 acres. The plans include the consolidation and control of the five rivers that water the department and a series of tunnels, eighteen miles in length, by which water will be conducted from a storage reservoir on

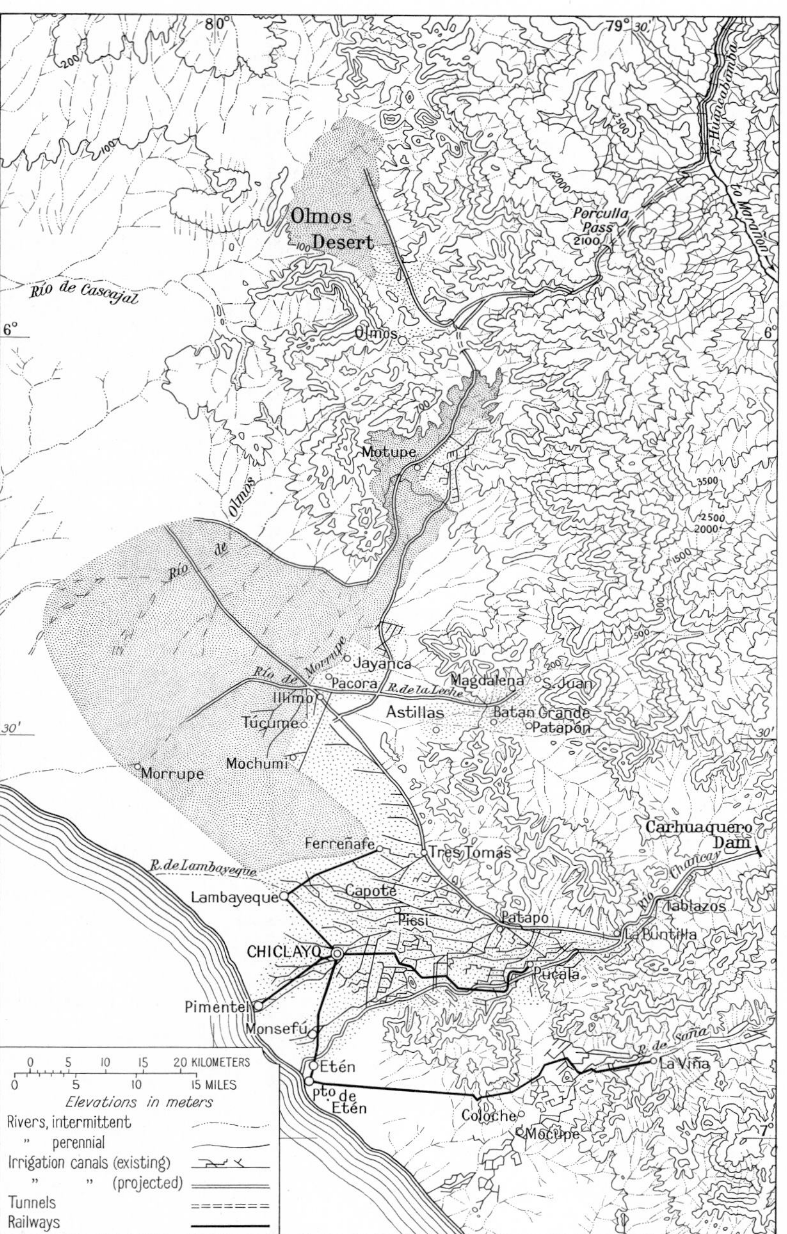

Fig. 14—The Lambayeque Irrigation Project. Approximate areas now under perennial or seasonal irrigation are shown by open stipple; approximate extent of new land to be brought under irrigation, by close stipple.

the Huancabamba River, a tributary of the Amazon system, through the main cordillera of the Andes to the Pacific slope. So far the work has consisted chiefly in constructing the dams, reservoirs, and new canals on the Pacific side of the Cordillera which will consolidate the present irrigation systems; but much land has already been reclaimed from the desert as a result of this work. Figures 15 and 16, photographs from an aerial survey of the project reproduced here by the courtesy of Mr. Charles W. Sutton, former Chief of the Irrigation Commission of Piura and Lambayeque, show the contrast between plantings of newly reclaimed land and the still unirrigated desert. A similar project of bringing water through the Cordillera of the Andes to the arid Pacific coast from the rivers of the Atlantic slope has been proposed and surveyed for the Iça Valley south of Pisco.

These and other plans of the Government for increasing the area of irrigated land in the coastal valleys are all part of one of the most interesting schemes that has ever been proposed for building up a citizenry of small landowners. It is planned to confine the work for the present chiefly to the

FIG. 15—Lambayeque once stood in the midst of the richest irrigated tract of the whole of Peru. It was then the capital and chief town of the department, and its fine parks and large churches and other buildings remain as evidence that it has seen better days. Floods have destroyed a large part of its old irrigation system; part has fallen into disuse because of lack of water. Today the desert touches the edge of the town, and its population has dwindled until it has now not more than 8000 people; while Chiclayo, the present capital, has 20,000. Undoubtedly some of the former prosperity of the town will return to it when the desert that borders it is reclaimed by irrigation.

FIG. 16—A new irrigation canal in the Department of Lambayeque with the first plantings of rice on its left and the still unirrigated desert on its right. These new plantings are on the Muy Finca hacienda—one of the largest estates of the department. The canal is fed by the Chancay River—the most important river of the department and, at present, its chief source of water for irrigation purposes. The recently constructed Carhuaquero dam and reservoir (see Fig. 14) have been so effective in conserving the water of this river and in controlling its flow that many acres of land long desert now have a full perennial supply of water for irrigation.

coastal valleys, where there is easy access to local markets and to ocean shipping, rather than to attempt to colonize regions east of the Andes, where tremendous difficulties of acclimatization and problems of transportation would be involved, and to create new land in them by increasing the supply of water for irrigation rather than to confiscate and divide the large estates as has been the recent policy in Mexico and in parts of Central Europe.

A REPRESENTATIVE SECTION OF THE WESTERN BORDER OF THE ANDES

For his photographs of the western border of the Peruvian Andes, Lieutenant Johnson has chosen the section between the port of Mollendo and the lofty, snow-capped volcanic crests overlooking the city of Arequipa (see map, Fig. 17). No section could have been chosen which would be more representative of the character of the western border of the Peruvian plateau. For there are assembled, as in a great composite picture, the features that one may see along the full length of the plateau margin. There are displayed the coastal terraces in one of their widest and best-preserved sections, the coast ranges in their boldest development, the high desert pampas that lie between the Coast Range and the foot of the Andes, interior valleys with a rich, alluvial soil and an abundance of water, and, in the background, the remarkably smooth line of the plateau edge with remnants of old volcanoes rising in great irregularity above it.

There, also, is to be seen an excellent cross section of the life of the people of western Peru: shepherds on high-level pasture lands at the summit of the plateau; small farms perched on narrow, terraced lands at valley heads; broad estates in the valley of the Chili River with a city in their midst that has all that mixture of modern life and century-old tradition that is the charm of many of the cities of the west coast republics; and a railway—one of the only two railways of Peru that penetrate from the coast to the plateau—leading down to a bare little port which, uninspiring as it may appear and isolated from all but the most drab of human activities is the gateway to one of the most important sections of the Andean plateau.

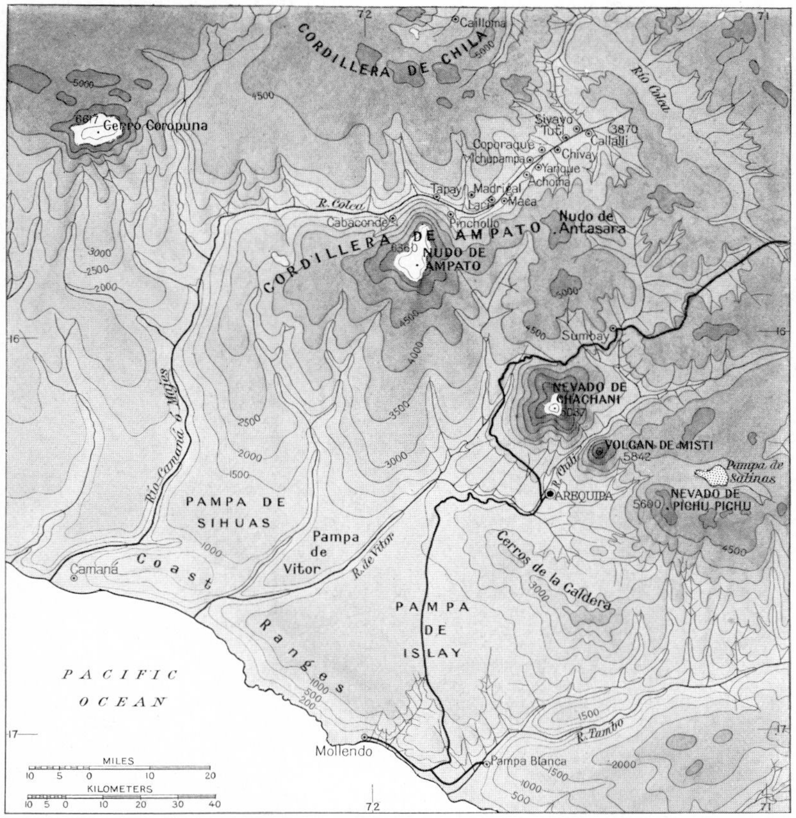

This is, moreover, the best-known section of the Peruvian Andes. It lies along the most frequently traveled route to the interior—the Southern Railway of Peru which not only connects Cuzco with Arequipa and Mollendo but is also one of the principal outlets for La Paz and northern Bolivia. Most of the features shown in the aerial photographs of the region have been described or photographed many times from the ground and will appear to many as familiar scenes viewed from a new angle.

FIG. 17—Map showing the region in which the aerial photographs of the western border of the Andes were made.

THE COASTAL TERRACES AT MOLLENDO

Broad coastal terraces form the border of the land at Mollendo. In the accompanying photographs (Fig. 18, taken as the plane rose from the sea for its flight into the Andes; and Fig. 19, taken as it approached the summit of the Coast Range) they may be studied in their full width from wave-cut shore to inner margin against the foot of the Coast Range. These upraised and dissected terraces of marine origin border the entire coast of Peru. Attention is called to them many times in the legends and notes accompanying the photographs of the coast in this volume. Their wave-cut outer edges and the cliffs and coves at the base of the Coast Range or coastal hills and spurs that border their inner margins are, in many places, scarcely less easily distinguishable than those to be seen at the

FIG. 18—An aerial photograph of Mollendo showing the full width of the smooth, little-dissected, lower coastal terrace (here about two and a half miles wide) and, in the background, the much-dissected upper terrace and the foot of the Coast Range. The lower terrace gets practically no rain, and, as a result, the streams that project themselves across it have cut steep-walled *quebradas* with no tributaries from the interfluves between them. These interfluves are rock-surfaced and flat except where marked by shallow, notch-like, seaward-facing slopes, which point to halts in the uplift, and smooth depressions without outlets such as are produced by sea action.

FIG. 19—A view from the air near Mollendo across the Coast Range and the high pampas which lie between it and the Andes, with a bit of the upper coastal terrace in the lower left corner. The dissection which this upper terrace is undergoing is in strong contrast to the smooth interfluves of the lower terrace. That it is more strongly dissected than the lower terrace is due not alone to its greater age and height (its inner margin is about 2400 feet high while that of the lower terrace is about 1500 feet) but also to the more immediate influence upon it of streams from the Coast Range. In addition, unlike the lower terrace, it receives considerable precipitation in the form of mist.

present shore line. In many places the wave-rolled materials of their upper surfaces and the details of their structure and relief seem as fresh as though they had been but yesterday lifted above the sea.

At most points two marine terraces, representing two periods of uplift with an intervening period of subsidence, are to be seen. At Mollendo, where the terraces are particularly wide and well developed, with a combined width of nearly four miles, the whole story of their formation can be read. Alluvial deposits laid down at the base of the Coast Range were planed by the sea. Uplift and dissection by streams followed. Then came another period of subsidence and of deposition, which almost completely obliterated the evidences of dissection. A final uplift, with streams again actively at the work of dissection, brings the history of the terraces to our own time.

AREQUIPA AND ITS BACKGROUND OF VOLCANIC PEAKS

From the sea at Mollendo, where the flight began, nothing of the Andes is visible, for the high wall of the Coast Range fills the background. But when the plane has risen to the level of the summits of the Coast Range a rare view is to be had across its gentle slopes and graded profiles and the rolling surface of the high pampas to the sharp, snow-capped summits of old volcanoes perched on the edge of the plateau. (See Figures 113 to 119.)

Once past the Coast Range the flight to the very edge of the valley in which the city of Arequipa lies is across the high pampas. These are piedmont surfaces rising gently toward the foot of the Andes from the inner border of the Coast Range, uplifted now several thousand feet and cut by the deep canyons of rivers flowing from the Andes to the sea. They are almost completely desertic except for patches of sparse, drought-resisting grasses. Dunes or irregular drifts of sand, banks of white earth (the so-called *tierra blanca*), and a pavement of sand-scoured pebbles a few inches thick cover the greater part of their surface. The only relief from the monotony of a flight across them is the narrow ribbons of green along stream beds in the widely separated canyon bottoms. But the snowy crests of the Cordillera loom always on the eastern horizon, and, when the plane has reached the inner border of the pampas, there unfolds a sudden entrancing vision of the irrigated valley of the Chili River with the red roofs of Arequipa in the midst of green fields and with snow-capped Chachani, El Misti, and Pichu-Pichu set amphitheater-like around it.

To quote Lord Bryce, "No eastern city has a mountain landscape like this. One must place Tunis or Trebizond in the valley of Zermatt to get an impression of Arequipa as it stands encircled by snow fields and towers of rock." Previous to the Conquest the site of the city was occupied by a rest station on the old Inca Road from Cuzco to the sea. Pizarro, recognizing the need of a stronghold between the interior and the coast, found the Chili Valley an ideal location with its rich alluvial soil, its abundance of water, and its command of one of the best passes to the interior of the plateau and established there a settlement which grew rapidily in wealth and culture. Today the Southern Railway of Peru connects Cuzco, the ancient Inca capital, with the port of Mollendo, following much the same route taken by the couriers of the Incas; and Arequipa is, in size, the third city of Peru and has long been the market and distributing center not only for the southern interior departments of the country but for a considerable part of northern Bolivia as well.

From the air, as from the ground, the old volcanoes with their great variety of size and form appear to dominate the landscape in this section of the Peruvian Andes. Their ragged profiles and steep slopes, capped with glistening snow during much of the year, catch and hold the eye, whether seen from a distance or close at hand. From a

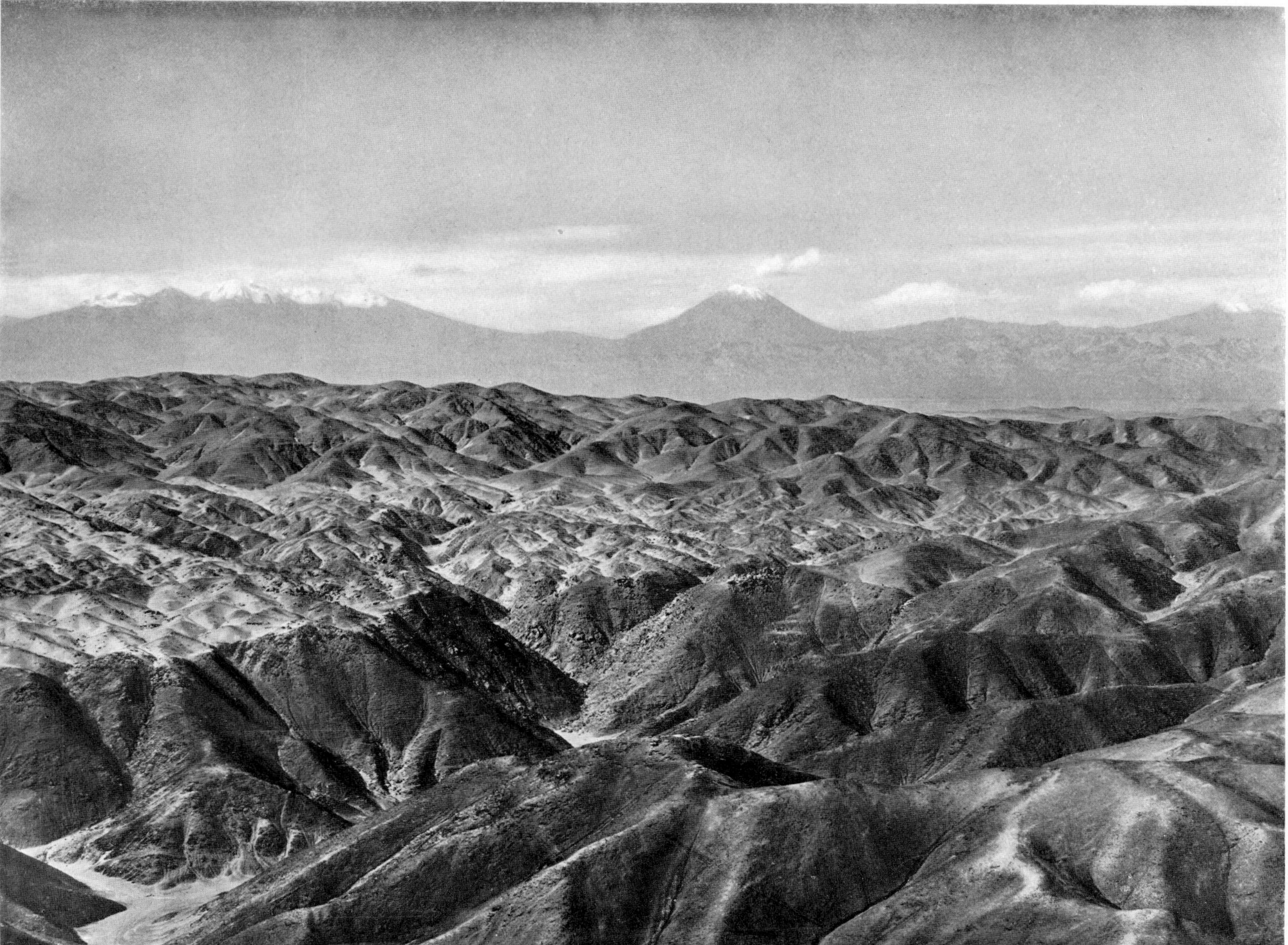

Fig. 20—A view across the Cerros de la Caldera (see map, Fig. 17) to the Chili Valley with the volcanic crests of Chachani, El Misti, and Pichu-Pichu in line from left to right along the edge of the plateau in the background.

FIG. 21—A view of El Misti from the west with the irrigated valley of the Chili River and the city of Arequipa at its foot. El Misti is the only volcano in this part of the Andes that still retains its symmetrical conical shape. (For other photographs of the volcano see Figs. 122 to 128.)

distance they are seen as the culminating points of a tremendous mountain wall rising to heights of more than 19,000 feet. They really stand, however, only a thousand feet or so above the general level of the plateau and, if set down at sea level, would hardly be recognized as a mountain range at all. Their insignificance, as compared with the mountain wall they surmount, is still better understood when one realizes that this wall is only half within the view even when seen from the shore. Its foot stands more than 20,000 feet beneath the sea. Nowhere in the world are there mountains so continuously lofty so near a coast dropping off to such abyssal depths as the Andes of southern Peru and northern Chile.

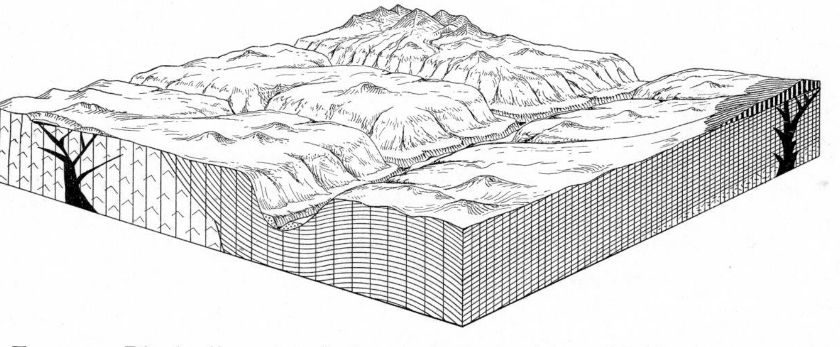

FIG. 22—Block diagram of the typical physiographic features of the western border of the Peruvian Andes—an extensive system of high-level, well graded, mature slopes, cut by deep canyons with steep, and in many places cliffed sides and narrow floors and surmounted by the remains of old volcanoes. At the valley heads are all the characteristic features of glacial erosion, and in the valley bottoms is a deep alluvial fill formed during the glacial period and now in process of dissection.

Close at hand there is a never-failing fascination in the varied forms of these old volcanoes. All have been long inactive. Even El Misti, the youngest of them, has not been actually in eruption since the Conquest, although at times smoke is seen rising from its crater. El Misti alone has retained its symmetrical form. All the others have more or less lost their original shapes under the prolonged action of ice and snow, although Pichu-Pichu on its northeasterly flanks still preserves remnants of the steep, smooth slopes of its once great cone. All, except El Misti, have been sculptured by ice and snow into a maze of serrate ridges and sharp peaks, scalloped with glacial cirques and bordered by a full complement of glacial features—hanging valleys, reversed slopes, moraines, and valley trains. The glaciers seem now to have disappeared except on Ampato, but erosion is continued by the process of nivation. All bear snow on at least their upper slopes during much of the year, although only Ampato has large permanent snow fields. On El Misti and even on Pichu-Pichu the snow disappears for at least a short period almost every year. Even Chachani has only a small cap that can be classed as truly permanent snow, and there are exceptional years in which this all but disappears.

THE PLATEAU SUMMIT

These old volcanoes are the center of attraction in the majority of the aerial photographs of this section of Peru (Figs. 122 to 142), for they are spectacular as compared with the generally monotonous surface of the plateau and are landmarks even more conspicuous to the aviator than to one who sees them from the ground. But they must be recognized even in the photographs as evidently far less significant in the geological history of the Andes than the broad, well graded surfaces from which they rise. These are the truly impressive features of the Andean landscape, these gently molded, mature surfaces which must have been produced close to sea level before they were uplifted to their present elevation. They form wide sections of the plateau summit at elevations of from 14,000 to 16,000 feet where one would expect to find only rugged mountain crests. They are interpreted as the result of prolonged denudation in an erosion cycle which persisted through the greater part of the Tertiary Period and ended in uplifts totaling many

FIG. 23—A section of the south side of the deep canyon of the Colca River. The snow-capped crests at the top of the photograph are part of the great mountain mass called the Nudo de Ampato (see Figs. 134 and 136), the highest peaks of which lie just beyond the photograph at the right. The village on the valley floor is probably Pinchollo (see map, Fig. 17). Shepherds' huts and corrals can be seen in sheltered valleys just below the edge of the graded surface of the plateau summit. Trails, white against the dark canyon walls, wind precipitously down to the valley bottom.

Fig. 24—Another view of the canyon of the Colca River, upstream from Figure 23, with a narrow tributary canyon entering from the south. The trail which zigzags down the canyon wall near the center of the photograph illustrates the manner in which the villages of the valley are connected with stations on the Southern Railway above Arequipa (see map, Fig. 17). To reach these villages by such a trail one travels by way of a high pass among the snow crests down a steep cirque at a glaciated valley head, across a rocky terminal moraine, down a stairlike trail cut in the canyon wall, and finally over numerous alluvial fans and around sharp spurs between them to the floor of the main valley.

FIG. 25—A sketch made from a section of Figure 23 enlarged to show the location and character of the corrals in sheltered valleys just below the plateau edge. There is considerable pasturage on the smooth slopes close to the corrals, and trails up the valley lead to the graded, grassy slopes of the volcano-crowned plateau summit.

thousands of feet and probably still in progress. Beneath them canyons and gorges with steep, cliffed walls, falling away to depths as great as 7000 feet, add to the evidence of erosion stimulated by recent uplift.

THE GORGE OF THE COLCA RIVER

In Figure 22, the principal topographic types produced by uplift and erosion in this section of the Andes are shown together in diagrammatic form. The aerial photographs (Figs. 23 and 24) present them scarcely less ideally. One needs no better examples than these of the value of aerial photography in the study of mountain landscapes. For a picture of what uplift and erosion, outpourings of lava, and the advance and retreat of glaciers have wrought in topographic forms and in the life of the Andean people, one need no longer piece together photographs taken from point to point as one descends the steep trail from a snowy pass between the high ranges that surmount the plateau down to the deep valley bottom. From the sharp, snow-capped crests looming against the sky at the top of these photographs to the fields and villages of the valley floor is a descent of quite two miles—twice the depth of the Grand Canyon; yet from the air the camera has caught the whole scene in a single photograph.

These and the succeeding photographs of the same region were taken by Lieutenant Johnson at the end of his flight among the volcanic crests that cap the plateau north of Arequipa. His pilot had flown him northward from Pichu-Pichu for some seventy miles, and they were about to swing westward for photographs of Ampato and Chachani when they came suddenly to the edge of the deep gorge of the Colca River. Around them, stretching away on all sides to the horizon, lay the smooth slopes of the plateau summit—cold, monotonous, and lifeless, broken here and there by narrow irregular ranges and isolated peaks, their ragged crests capped with snow. Beneath them a steep-walled canyon dropped away thousands of feet to a narrow valley floor filled from wall to wall with a patchwork of fields in countless shades of vivid green set close with neatly-laid-out villages. The photographs caught thus by accident are the most spectacular of the whole series and perhaps the most interesting.

One gets an impression of youthfulness and motion from these photographs, as though the tremendous uplifts that raised the plateau to its present elevation were still in progress. Only at the summit are there evidences of age. Gentle, waste-cloaked slopes that could only have been formed close to sea level cover wide sections of it. Above them, masses of rock of greater original elevation and greater resistance to denudation rise in narrow ranges carved by snow and ice to sharp peaks and ridges. Below them, streams (fed by the snow fields of the higher slopes) have cut deep gorges and are still vigorously at work, deepening their beds and dissecting the smooth interstream summits. But, deep as are the gorges that these streams have cut, their work has just begun. Between them the summit surfaces seem as yet scarcely touched. The zone of "topographic unconformity" that marks the break between the two erosion cycles, between the gentle gradients of the summit and the steep gradients of the young gorges, is still one of the most conspicuous features of the landscape.

FARMERS AND SHEPHERDS OF THE COLCA VALLEY

On the plateau summits, between the lofty mountains which rise above them and the edge of the deep valleys sunk far below them, Indian shepherds pasture their flocks of sheep and alpacas. Their huts and corrals can be seen in Figure 23 in the lee of cliffs just below the edge of the plateau, where they are protected from the violent winds which frequently sweep its summit. Over the higher slopes they lead their flocks easily from the plateau edge to the very border of the snow fields. *Ichu*, the coarse, tufted forage grass of the Andes, furnishes pasturage, and there are also shorter grasses on the moister slopes. Brooks and springs are everywhere within easy reach.

These shepherds' huts are among the world's highest human habitations. In the photograph no cultivated fields are to be seen near them, although the slopes on which they stand seem not too steep for cultivation and water could easily be brought to irrigate them. They must be, therefore, at an elevation where there is too much frost even for potato-growing, the upper limit of which, in this section of the Andes, is at about 14,000 feet. The first cultivated land is to be seen at some distance below them—a few terraced strips on small alluvial fans at the mouths of minor tributaries to the main valleys. As the main valley bottom is approached the fans are larger and there is progressively

FIG. 26—A closer view of the village shown on the valley floor in Figure 23. The village is typically Spanish-American, with its streets laid out in rectangular pattern around a church and central plaza. In the foreground is the inner valley now being cut by the Colca River in the alluvial fill of the valley floor, terraced down to the very edge of the river. At the right a broad white road leads down the valley to connect the village with others on the valley floor. In the center foreground a narrow trail leads from the village down the terraces of the inner valley to the river.

FIG. 27—A broader view of the section of the main valley shown in the foreground of Figure 24. The river must be rapidly deepening its channel, yet its inner valley is terraced in places down to the water's edge. It is probable that as rapidly as the river deepens its bed and so provides new and easily irrigated land, the higher terraces that extend well up the slopes above the main valley floor are abandoned. In many places the higher terraces show only faintly in contrast to the fresh appearance of those on the valley floor and along the sides of the inner valley.

FIG. 28—The group of villages at the upper end of the main valley of the Colca River (see map, Fig. 17). There are five villages in this photograph, each with its church and plaza. The complete occupation of the flat land of the terraces by farms accentuates the relief. But for the alluvial fill of the glacial period the whole region would be pasture land only. It is a striking feature of the better-favored valleys that they are so completely occupied with fields that a larger population cannot find support except by diminishing the per capita food supply or by part-time employment elsewhere.

more water for irrigation, until on the valley floor every possible foot of land is irrigated and cultivated and terraces extend far up the fans and even up the sides of the spurs between them.

Barley and potatoes are grown at the higher levels (barley up to 13,000 feet, potatoes to 14,000). Farther down in the valley, as the climate becomes successively milder and the frost-free season longer, other crops are added. Wheat ripens at 12,000 feet, corn at 11,000. On the valley floor, which is here between 8000 and 10,000 feet above sea level, there are probably orchards of temperate-zone fruits and vineyards.

The valley must be densely populated for, although it is narrow, the towns stand close together and are fair-sized. Maps of the valley show fourteen towns in a distance of less than forty miles. Except for the shepherds all of the people of the valley live in these towns. Between the valley floor and the shepherds' huts near the top of the canyons there are no houses. The more prosperous farmers have their fields close at hand on the rich fill of the valley floor. The poorer farmers must climb by steep trails to bits of fields laboriously terraced on alluvial fans far up the canyons. The poorest of all are the shepherds at the top of the country for, wherever there is a frost-free season long enough to ripen crops and water enough for irrigation, arable land is too valuable to be used for pasture.

Even before the Conquest these agricultural communities hidden away in intermont basins, little known to the outside world, approachable only by precipitous trails, constituted an important element in the population of the Peruvian Andes. Today they supply food, clothing, and pack animals to near-by mining districts. Wherever there are mining districts in the Peruvian Andes there are to be found these agricultural groups in high-level, sheltered valleys near by.

THE CHANCHAMAYO VALLEY

San Ramón (Fig. 30) in the Chanchamayo Valley is a frontier settlement of the Peruvian montaña—the forested slopes and valleys of the eastern border of the Andes. Where two streams from the Andes join to form one of the great tributaries of the Amazon system (see map, Fig. 29) they have built up a broad flood plain. A road enters this flood plain from the valley at the top of the photograph, crosses one of the streams by a narrow suspension bridge near their junction, and continues on down the valley. Flood plain, road, and bridge together make the site a natural one for the location of a village. The fertile, easily tilled soil of the flood plain will support a considerable population. The road provides an outlet for surplus products. The bridge is a natural place for pack trains from settlements farther down the valley to halt for rest if there is pasture there for animals and food and shelter for men.

Once the settlement is established the farmers on near-by plantations will find it a convenient place to organize their pack trains for trips up to the plateau, and *arrieros*, the muleteers of the Andes, will locate there with animals for hire. Buyers from the mining centers of the plateau or the towns of the coast will make the settlement their head-quarters. Merchants will set up shops there to supply the manufactured articles that the farmers of the valley need and cannot produce for themselves.

Thus the settlement will come to serve a purpose not unlike that of the ports of the Pacific coast. Like them, it will express in its size and its activity the prosperity of the region it serves. Like them, it will grow as more land is brought under cultivation in near-by valleys or the traffic to and from more distant settlements increases.

There is no lack of water in these valleys of the eastern border of the Andes as in the valleys of the coastal desert. The streams shown in the photograph are full, rushing torrents. There is abundant rainfall throughout the year, the so-called rainy season from November to April being

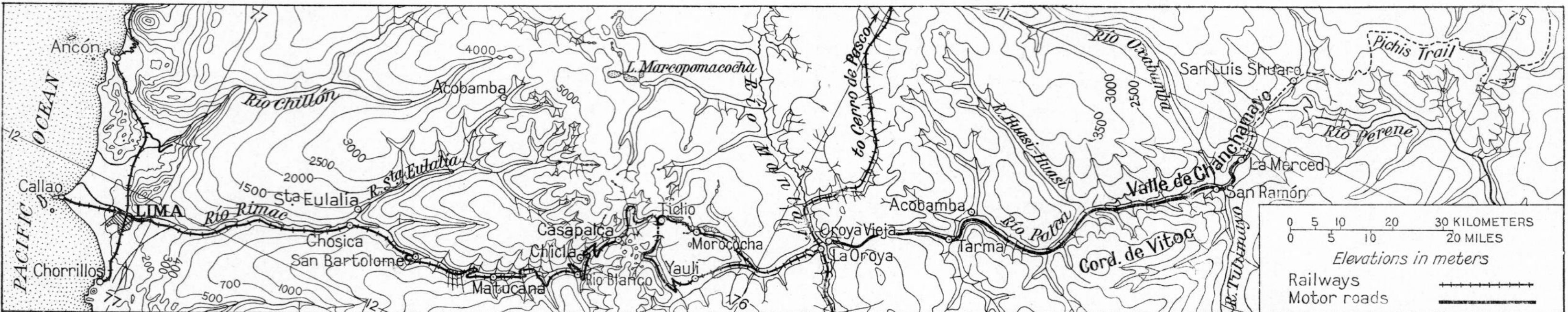

FIG. 29—Map showing the route by rail and motor road from Lima to the Chanchamayo Valley. The trail leading out of La Merced is the famous Pichis trail to Puerto Bermudez, the head of navigation on the Pichis River and the starting point of the river route to Iquitos.

only the season of heavier and more continuous rain. Parts of the Chanchamayo Valley are in the rain shadow of the hills that border it and consequently require irrigation during at least the drier season, but the streams furnish at all times a full flow of water to the irrigation ditches. There is no lack of arable land as in many of the valleys of the western border of the Andes, and the climate makes possible a great variety of tropical crops; yet, in the area covered by this photograph, even the most easily cultivated land of the flood plain and the lower slopes of the hills is not more than half in crops. Having seen how precious water is in the coastal valleys and how, wherever there is water there for irrigation, every foot of arable land is cultivated to its full capacity, one must wonder to see so much waste land in this photograph. But distances, not only to the markets of the coastal region but even to the mining centers of the plateau, are too great and means of transportation still too costly to permit the settlement of colonists in any large numbers in these eastern valleys in spite of their fertility and their abundance of rainfall. (See also Figs. 137 to 143.)

THE MOTOR ROAD TO THE CHANCHAMAYO VALLEY

The most important feature caught by the camera in this aerial photograph of the site of San Ramón is, therefore, the road. The roads leading down from the plateau are scarcely less vital to the development of the eastern valleys of Peru than is water for irrigation to the development of the coastal valleys. Most of them are only the roughest of trails, passable only for pack animals; but they provide a means, however slow and difficult, by which some portion of the products of the valleys can be carried up to the pleateau and manufactured articles brought back in exchange. The relative prosperity of these valleys and their attractiveness to settlers depend almost entirely upon the character of the roads which connect them with the plateau and their proximity to roads and railways leading down from the plateau to the coast.

It is due to the character of the road down to the Chanchamayo Valley and to the fact that it connects on the plateau not only with railways to important mining centers but also to a through rail route to the Pacific coast, that this valley is today the most prosperous of all the eastern valleys of Peru. The road is a motor road seventy-nine miles long connecting La Merced, a settlement eight miles down the valley beyond San Ramón, with Oroya, the terminus of the main line of the Central Railway of Peru and the

FIG. 30—The village of San Ramón photographed from the northeast. Here the Tulumayo River, coming in from the left of the photograph, joins the Palca or Tarma River to form the Perené. There is abundant rainfall here, but so intense is the heat of the afternoon sun that the northern and western slopes of the hills that border the valley do not retain sufficient moisture to support tree growth. Only in the gulleys and on the sides of the spurs that are shaded from the afternoon sun is there forest. The more exposed slopes have a cover of thick grass. In the photograph the line between grassland and forest is so sharp as to give the impression that the grasslands are artificial clearings.

starting point for branch lines to the mining districts of Cerro de Pasco and Huancavelica.

It is a good road, kept in good repair, but narrow. There are few places in it where wheeled vehicles can pass. Automobiles are permitted to go up and down it only on alternate days. In many places it passes so close to the edge of steep precipices that the slightest carelessness on the part of the driver may send an automobile tumbling down to the river a thousand feet or more below. The numerous bridges by which it crosses the streams tributary to the main valley are frail suspension structures barely wide enough to accommodate a single vehicle, and the loads that may be carried over them are strictly regulated. Yet it is one of the most important roads in Peru; not so much because of the traffic it carries, although traffic on it is heavy during certain seasons of the year, but because it is the only road for wheeled vehicles between the plateau and the eastern valley region. To the people of Peru, moreover, it is a symbol of the coming of the day, long dreamed of, when these fertile, well-watered eastern valleys will support a prosperous agricultural population and when roads and railways will carry their products to the cities of the plateau and the coast and down to the ports to swell the volume of the country's export trade.

SETTLEMENT AND TRANSPORTATION IN THE EASTERN VALLEYS AND LOWLANDS

It should be an indication to them, also, that the need of new land for settlement and the demands of the plateau and coastal markets or the export trade are not yet sufficiently pressing to force the construction of the roads and railways necessary before the colonization of the eastern valleys can be successfully carried out. The Chanchamayo Valley was one of the first of these valleys to attract settlers. By the end of the seventeenth century it was famous throughout the country for its prosperous plantations. A revolt of the Indians of the region in 1742 wiped out the plantations; and for more than a century thereafter, until in 1847 San Ramón was established as a fort and garrison, settlers slowly returning to the valley were constantly menaced. By that time the restoration of the irrigation systems of the coastal valleys was well under way, and there was no longer sufficient need for the products of the eastern valleys to attract settlers to them in large numbers.

San Ramón has today a population of only about three hundred; and La Merced, the most easterly settlement in the valley, about eight hundred. The well-known colony of the Peruvian Corporation on the Perené River has made important progress as an experimental colony, but its products have as yet no significant place in the markets of the country. In spite of the fact that motor road and railway provide the Chanchamayo Valley with a two-day transportation route to Lima, the cultivated areas are still widely scattered and limited to the most easily worked land —coffee plantations here and there on flat-topped spurs, plantations of sugar cane, tropical fruits, and some cotton on valley flats. Coffee and alcohol, the latter made from sugar cane, are the principal exports, for their value is such in relation to their bulk and weight that they can support the heavy transportation costs and still return a profit.

Elsewhere such products of the eastern valleys as find their way to the plateau and the coast must be carried out on muleback and, in some cases, on the backs of Indian bearers, for, although there has been no lack of plans for roads and railways, only this one road has been completed. Even it was not built primarily to serve the Chanchamayo Valley. It was built as a link in the land-and-water route for travelers, mail, and freight between Lima and Iquitos on the Amazon River—the remotest frontier settlement of Peru. From La Merced the land route is continued by a trail which winds up over the foothills of the Andes and down to Puerto Burmudez (Fig. 31) on the Pichis River. Thence the route continues by motor boat and steam

FIG. 31—Puerto Bermudez, the head of launch navigation on the overland route from Lima to Iquitos, consists only of a few houses in a clearing in the jungle on the right bank of the Pichis River. Passengers and freight en route from Lima to Iquitos here leave the mules by which they have made the five-day trip from La Merced and are transferred to launches which carry them a thousand miles down the Pichis, Pachitea, and Ucayali rivers to Iquitos. The trip downstream takes from fifteen to seventeen days, upstream from nineteen to twenty-one. Now the navy planes which fly the route can make the trip from San Ramón to Iquitos (a distance of 1200 miles by trail and river) in two days. (See Fig. 33.)

Fig. 32—Masisea has long been a well known port for river steamers on the Ucayali River. Maps show it as an important town. In the aerial photograph it is seen to be only a few huts in a clearing on the river bank. The Peruvian government has maintained a wireless station here for some time, and the port has now taken on new importance as the mid-point station on the air route from San Ramón to Iquitos. The buildings of the airport can be seen in the center of the photograph. A hydroplane is anchored close to the shore. (See also Figs. 144 to 150.)

launch down the Pichis, Pachitea, and Ucayali rivers to the Amazon. Now the government maintains as well an airplane service for passengers and mail between San Ramón and Iquitos. Its hangars and landing field can be seen in the open space at the left of the photograph.

It was on a reconnaissance flight over a part of this air route that Lieutenant Johnson took the photographs of the Chanchamayo and adjacent valleys and of the lowlands of the Amazon Basin presented in this volume. Figure 32 is a photograph from the air of Masisea, the mid-station of the route and long a well known stopping place for steamers on the Ucayali River. Maps without exception indicate by symbols and lettering that it is an important town. From the air it is seen to be only a few huts in a clearing in the jungle forest on the river bank to which have recently been added houses for the personnel of the airport.

PERU: A LAND OF TOPOGRAPHIC AND CLIMATIC CONTRASTS

"This Land of Peru, which is of a strange nature amongst all others," thus Samuel Purchas translates the words with which José de Acosta introduces his description of the "very remarkeable properties" which aroused the wonder of the early visitors to Peru—properties which have, in the three centuries since de Acosta wrote his account, evoked a succession of descriptions quite as enthusiastic and filled with wonderment as his, though none perhaps has matched the picturesque language of the Purchas translation. Squier, nearly three hundred years later, wrote: "In no part of the world does nature assume grander, more imposing, or more vivid forms. Deserts as bare and repulsive as those of Sahara alternate with valleys as rich and luxuriant as those of Italy. Lofty mountains, crowned with eternal snow, lift high their rugged sides over broad, bleak *punas*, or table-lands, themselves more elevated than the summits of the White Mountains or of the Alleghanies. Rivers, taking their rise among melting snows, precipitate themselves through deep and rocky gorges into the Pacific, or wind, with swift but gentler current, among the majestic but broken Andes, to swell the flood of the Amazon."[3] It has been said of Peru that nowhere on the earth are greater physical contrasts compressed within such small spaces. It is difficult to construct a satisfactory picture of such a landscape from written descriptions. Photographs taken from the ground rarely afford the broad view needed if its features are to be seen complete and its relationships fully understood. For an adequate picture of it one must look upon it from the air as in the photographs presented in this volume.

It is in its diversity of topographic forms and climate and particularly in the influence of these on human life that the geographer finds the charm of Peru. Perhaps nowhere else in the world are there to be found within such short distances so many and such clear cases of environmental control. To the geologist, the botanist, and the zoölogist, no less than to the geographer, Peru is an interesting and fertile field of study. To all of these the aerial photographs reproduced in this volume must suggest a new and important means of research.

So well known are the relics of the empire of the Incas, and of the rulers who preceded them, which dot the landscape throughout the coastal region and the western part of the Andean plateau, that the interest of the archeologist in Peru and the value to him of the aerial photograph scarcely need mention here.

The story of the Spanish conquest of the Inca empire and the fabulous treasure carried back to Spain by the conquerors is probably better known to most than is the scarcely less spectacular and infinitely more important struggle of our own time to win for Peru a larger place in the markets of the world. Yet the hardships encountered by Pizarro and his followers are pale beside the labor and

[3] E. George Squier: Peru, Incidents of Travel and Exploration in the Land of the Incas, New York, 1877, p. 6.

loss of life that gave to Peru the highest railway in the world in order that the products of the copper and silver mines of the Cerro de Pasco region might be brought down to the sea. The project now well under way of tunneling through the Andes to tap the waters of the Amazon Basin for the coastal valleys of the Department of Lambayeque is a treasure quest with which the despoiling of the Incas cannot compare. For, charming as is Peru's diversity of topography, climate, and life to the scientist and the traveler, it has been not only a handicap to the development of the natural resources of the country but an impediment to the development of national solidarity as well. Not only does the great plateau of the Andes divide the whole country into three longitudinal strips of coastal desert, mountains, and eastern lowlands, difficult of access one to the other, but there are within these larger divisions many lesser but nevertheless important barriers of desert or jungle, steep-walled canyon or rugged mountain range, which more or less effectively isolate the country's areas of actual or potential resources.

PERU AS A FIELD FOR AIR TRANSPORTATION

As a result there are no broad areas of continuous population in Peru but a great many districts separated for the most part by physiographic barriers of such magnitude that the construction and maintenance of modern communication and transport connections between them and with the country's centers of economic and political administration have been too costly and difficult to be considered except in cases of the utmost necessity. The coast valleys are reasonably well served by short rail lines or roads to the nearest ocean port; but only two railways penetrate into the Andes, so that the greater part of the plateau and all of the eastern valleys and lowlands, except the Chanchamayo Valley, must still depend upon such slow and arduous means of transport and communication as the pack train and the river boat. These isolated districts have little exchange of products with each other and find only a limited market in the country's more important centers of population. Their problem, therefore, as far as transportation is concerned, is simply that of finding and developing the easiest possible route to the nearest possible ocean port.

Transportation by such routes is all too slow for the carrying of important mail; for hurrying the manager of an estate or a mine to the capital city for conferences with his superiors or with government officials; for bringing from the distant corners of the republic representatives to the national congress; or for rushing army officers and supplies to the defense of the government against the sporadic attempts at revolution that must still be anticipated in a country made up of isolated districts which have little relation with and consequently little understanding of each other.

Thus the airplane has found in Peru a country prepared by nature for its enthusiastic reception. In no other country of South America has the government moved so swiftly in the development of aviation or the people shown more lively interest in its progress. Air transportation has made remarkable progress in Peru when one considers how short is the time in which it has been on any sort of an organized basis. The first flight in Peru, made in 1910 by a Peruvian aviator, aroused the enthusiastic interest that might be expected of a people accustomed to travel involving long trips by muleback or at best by slow and infrequent trains and tiresome waiting at comfortless ports for the arrival of the coastwise steamer. That interest seems never to have flagged in spite of a succession of serious accidents in the eleven-year period between the first flight and 1921 when the President's son, Captain Juan Leguia, who had served in the British Royal Air Corps during the World War, established a naval air base at Ancón.

President Leguia, always concerned with the necessity, economic as well as strategic, of bringing the more distant and isolated sections of the country into closer communication with the seat of government, played a very important part in developing air-mindedness in his people. In 1924 the government began in earnest the organization of an air force and summoned an American mission under Commander H. B. Grow of the United States Navy to take charge. Since then flying services of the army and navy have been reorganized with Commander Grow as Inspector-General, the training bases improved, and new ones established. Meanwhile the government has encouraged commercial companies to establish regular passenger and mail routes connecting the towns of the coastal region; and two commercial companies, the Faucett Aviation Company and the Pan American-Grace Airways, now make regular weekly flights with mail and passengers from Lima to Talara and to Arequipa with stops at many intermediate points. In addition, the government itself has entered the field of commercial air transportation by establishing the service between San Ramón and Iquitos mentioned above and is planning to establish other lines between the eastern lowlands and points on the plateau that have access to the coast by road or railway.

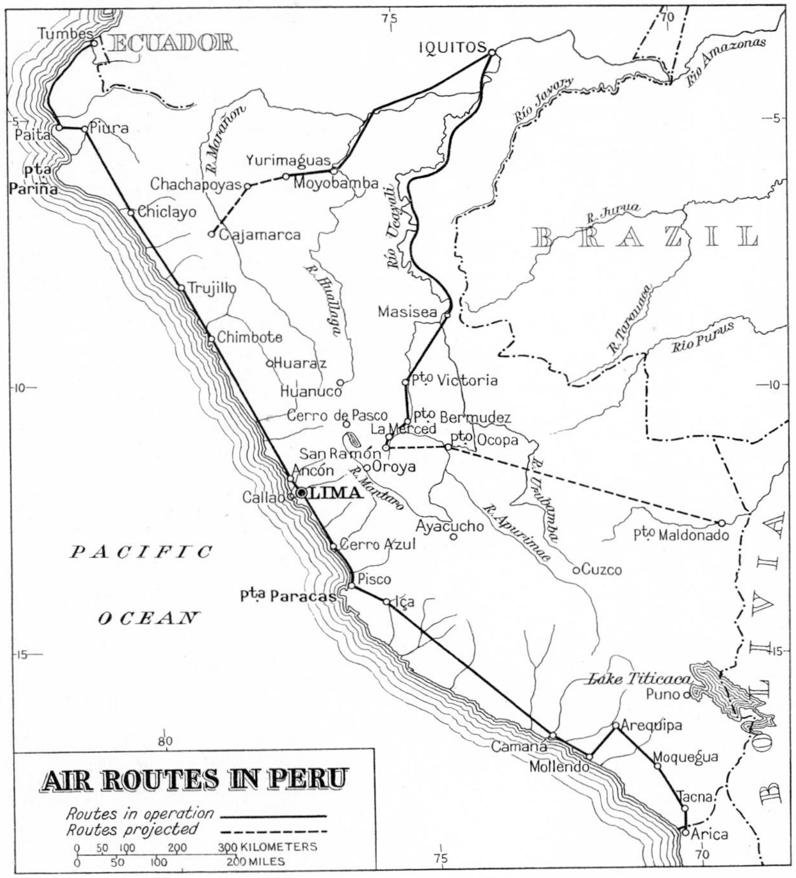

FIG. 33—Peru now has more than three thousand miles of air routes operated on regular schedules. The routes along the coast are operated by commercial companies. The Peruvian Navy operates the lines that bring the remote settlements of the eastern part of the republic into closer relationship with the cities and ports of the coast. The proposed Cajamarca-Iquitos line will connect the more important settlements of the northern part of the republic. The San Ramón-Puerto Maldonado route will bring the latter town within three days of Lima. The best route to it now is from Cuzco by difficult overland trails and canoes or rafts on rivers filled with rapids.

The purpose of this service must be considered as chiefly strategic, since the products of the region are too bulky for air transportation and there is no great movement of people within the region or between it and the coast. Yet, during the first year of the San Ramón-Iquitos line sixty-eight trips were made between San Ramón and Masisea, the midsection of the route on the Ucayali River, and ninety-two between Masisea and Iquitos, with a total of 2061 kilograms of mail and 304 kilograms of packages carried. One hundred thirty-three passengers were carried between San Ramón and Masisea, and one hundred forty-four between Masisea and Iquitos. Now a representative from Iquitos journeying to Lima to attend the National Congress can make the entire trip in three days; whereas, before the air service was established, it usually took more than a month by launch, canoe, muleback, motor, and train.

The "great contrarieties" remarked by the earliest European visitors to Peru still hold. To many a Peruvian who has never seen a wheeled vehicle of any sort and to many who have never even seen a pack animal the airplane is today a familiar sight.

AERIAL PHOTOGRAPHY AND MAPPING IN PERU

It is natural that, in a country so in need of air transportation and so enthusiastically committed to its use, the value of aerial photography for mapping purposes should have been early recognized. In many parts of Peru the study of areas of potential resources, the examination of sites for colonization projects, the location of transportation routes are prohibitively costly by the usual methods of ground survey. But the aerial camera, in a few hours of flying time, can cover more territory than could, in many parts of the country, be covered in as many months by the simplest type of reconnaissance survey on the ground. Now the photographic sections of the Peruvian army and navy air services and also several commercial companies located in Peru use the aerial camera for a great variety of purposes—for surveys of reservoir and dam sites in connection with irrigation projects in the coastal valleys, for the location of irrigable lands in the valleys themselves, for preliminary studies of and progress reports on road and railway construction projects. The Naval Air Service has mapped a large part of the coast. The Geographical Service of the army has contracted with a private company for aerial surveys to be incorporated in its new topographical map of the country.

In 1928 Lieutenant Johnson, who had had wide experience in aerial photography in the United States, was appointed Chief Photographer of the Naval Air Service and Instructor in Aerial Photography at the Ancón Naval Air Base. The photographs published in this volume are evidence of his success in developing a technique adapted to conditions in Peru. A brief description of his equipment and methods may be of value to others interested in aerial photography under similar conditions.

The camera used for the oblique photographs was the Fairchild Aerial camera Model K–6 equipped with a Zeiss Tessar lens of F. 5 aperture and twenty inches focal length. For vertical photography the Fairchild Model K–3, with a Zeiss Tessar lens of F. 4.5 aperture and twelve inches focal length was used. Filters Aero 1, Aero 2, and Minus Blue were used, Aero 2 being used most and Minus Blue least. The unmounted gelatine type of filter was used at first but was unsatisfactory because of its tendency to buckle with changes in temperature and humidity and its susceptibility to mold. Filters mounted in glass and equipped with metal rims so that they could be locked in the lens barrel and quickly changed from one density to another were found to be the most satisfactory. Normal panchromatic film was found to be best adapted to conditions in Peru because it does not need to be kept on ice as does the hypersensitized panchromatic film. Even though shipments of the normal panchromatic film were received, on account of numerous delays, long after its development date was past, it gave good results until used up.

During the winter months the sun is rarely seen in the coastal region of Peru, where most of the photographic work was done, and, although the clouds were usually high enough for making oblique photographs at low altitudes, when verticals or obliques covering large areas were required, for which a working altitude of more than 1500 feet was needed, it was frequently necessary to wait for weeks until the clouds were high enough to work beneath them. When, under such conditions, it was not possible to wait, the method adopted was to fly low and make the exposures with considerably more than the usual sixty per cent overlap so that, in constructing the mosaic, all but the centers of the photographs, where the distortion was least, could be eliminated. When a large area had to be mapped under such conditions, as, for instance, the work on the new port terminal at Callao, of which photographs at regular intervals were required for the government records of progress, it was found that, by flying over the area many times and making exposures through rifts in the clouds wherever possible, the whole area could be satisfactorily covered.

Fig. 34—Pimentel, the chief port for the irrigated valleys of the Department of Lambayeque (see map, Fig. 14), lies on an open roadstead fully exposed to the surf. Its pier (1746 feet long), which is connected by rail with the important towns and haciendas of the department, is one of the longest on the coast. The town is in two sections. In the foreground of the photograph are the low, flat-roofed, wattle and mud-plaster houses of the stevedores and boatmen. Above the pier head are the modern summer homes of the wealthy residents of the department. North of the town and along its southern edge can be seen the channels of wet-season overflow streams from the delta of the Chancay River.

FIG. 35—The port of Etén, like Pimentel, is connected by rail with the irrigated valleys of the Department of Lambayeque and was formerly the chief port of the department. At all of the ports of Peru, except for a small amount of dockage space at Callao, ships must anchor well beyond the end of the pier and load and unload by means of launches; but Etén is particularly exposed to the prevailing southerly winds and at times the surf is so heavy as to halt all shipping operations. Etén is almost as barren as Supé, although around the abandoned salt pans (seen in the lower right corner of the photograph) there is some vegetation—probably salt grass.

FIG. 36—At Pacasmayo, the port for the Jequetepeque Valley, a high bluff (not shown in the photograph) protects the harbor on the south, making it the safest anchorage between Paita and Chimbote. The town, which is located at the mouth of the Pacasmayo River, a small stream having its source in a lagoon at the foot of the Andes a few miles back from the shore and entering the sea near the pier, is not the usual settlement of stevedores and boatmen only but contains several small factories and has, consequently, a more prosperous appearance than most of the Peruvian ports. The cemetery, drifted with sand, stands on the lower of two marine terraces visible from the sea.

Fig. 37—Huanchaco is connected by rail with the Chicama Valley and was for more than three hundred years the port for both the Chicama and Moche valleys. The surf, however, is particularly heavy there, as shown in the photograph, and the port is now abandoned on account of the better harbors and better port facilities at Salaverry and Puerto Chicama. The Rio Seco, a wet-season stream, has cut a wide channel through the lower of the two marine terraces visible at Huanchaco, building two terraces of its own on which the faint outlines of symmetrically laid-out fields, apparently now abandoned, can be seen. The old church back of the town has been a landmark for ships for centuries.

FIG. 38—Buenos Aires is the bathing resort for Trujillo, the chief urban center of the Moche or Chimú Valley, and the fourth largest city of Peru. Trujillo is situated two and a half miles inland from the resort and is connected with it by road and electric tramway. The Moche Valley was the center of the pre-Inca kingdom of the Great Chimú (see Figs. 11 and 12) and long before the Spanish Conquest had been brought to a state of agricultural development that has not yet been completely restored, although the valley is now the most important and highly developed of the coastal valleys of northern Peru and produces nearly half the sugar output of the country.

FIG. 39—Moche, in its setting of rich green cane, rice, and cotton fields backed by the foothills of the Andes and reaching down so close to the shore that the surf appears to break at their very edge, is a favorite summer resort for the whole Moche or Chimú Valley today as it was in the days of the Great Chimú. Gardens abound throughout the town, not only on the estates of the well-to-do, as shown in the foreground of the photograph, but also in the enclosed patios of the more closely built section. The town lies on the lower coastal terrace midway between Trujillo and the port of Salaverry near the mouth of the Moche, the principal river of the valley.

Fig. 40—Cerro Carretas, the headland shown in this photograph, forms the cove in which is located the port of Salaverry, now the chief port for the Chicama and Moche valleys with which it is connected by rail. The settlement lies just behind the headland at the right of the photograph, and the pier has been built close along its inner edge. At best the headland forms only a small embayment and affords but slight protection from wind and swell; but it is to this slight protection that the location here of the chief port of the Chicama and Moche valleys is due. The coast in front of these valleys is open and unprotected. Their port, therefore, has been located on the nearest embayment.

Fig. 41—A broader view of the headland shown in Figure 40, with Cerro de la Garita in the background at the right. Salaverry lies at the southernmost tip of the Moche Valley and marks the southern limit of the region of broad coastal *pampas* of northern Peru. South of Trujillo the foothills of the Andes begin to approach the coast, and the plain narrows rapidly. At Moche it appears from the sea as only a narrow strip of green backed by high hills, and in the headland that protects the port of Salaverry on the south the foothills of the Andes rise directly from the sea. From there on to Cerro Azul the only irrigable land is the alluvial fans and deltas between the spurs of the Andes.

Fig. 42—A continuation eastward of Cerro Carretas. Two marine terraces can be seen at Salaverry. The lower, on which the town is built, is about one-half mile wide and is only from five to ten feet high. The upper is from one hundred seventy-five to two hundred feet above the sea and is much more modified by wind action there than elsewhere to the north. Huge, shapeless masses of sand in places and well formed dunes in others give it a very irregular surface. In this photograph the edge of the upper terrace has been obscured by the sand that has been carried by the wind well up toward the top of the hill, but the edge of the lower terrace close to the shore is remarkably well defined.

FIG. 43—Cerro de la Garita (3720 feet), the high hill shown in the background of the preceding photographs of the port of Salaverry. Sand blown up from the narrow coastal plains covers the hill almost to its top, obscuring all evidence of the marine terraces to be found elsewhere back of the port. Salaverry is, and probably has been since pre-colonial times, the chief center in Peru for the manufacture of salt by evaporating from sea water. The salt is evaporated in open vats made by digging shallow trenches in the low coastal plain to which sea water is brought by means of narrow canals. The photograph shows some of the vats now apparently abandoned.

FIG. 44—North Island of the Guañape Islands, one of the groups of guano islands off the coast of Peru. The dark patches on the island consist entirely of birds. All the way down the coast great flocks of these birds are to be seen swooping down by thousands to feed on the schools of fish with which the cool waters of the Humboldt Current teem. The fertility of the coastal valleys is in large part due to the easily available fertilizer provided by these guano islands. The work of extracting the guano was under way when the photograph was taken. Men can be seen at work at the upper end of the island, and trucks coming and going on the roads leading down to the pier. (See note 1, page 157.)

Fig. 45—A view from the north of Santa Head and the little port of Santa with the tip of Coisco Island in the background at the left. Santa Head (445 feet) is virtually an island. Only a narrow neck of low land covered with lagoons invaded by the sea at high tide ties it to the mainland. The port and town of Santa, the latter about two miles inland on the edge of the irrigated delta of the Santa River, were once of considerable importance, the port serving for many years as the shipping point for the products of the haciendas of the delta, but they have now been supplanted by Chimbote, which has better protection for shipping and railway connections with the delta.

FIG. 46—Santa Head and the port of Santa with the lagoon-filled isthmus that joins the promontory to the mainland in the foreground. The vicinity of the port abounds in ruins of the pre-colonial civilizations. On the hill in the foreground can be seen an elaborate system of terraces, now abandoned, leading up to the ruins of a fortress on the crest. These hilltop fortresses surrounded by terraced farms were a common feature of the line of defense maintained along the coast road by the Inca rulers and their predecessors. The *garuas*, the winter mists which are often so heavy on this section of the coast as to shut out the sun for weeks at a time, furnished the moisture for the crops cultivated on the terraces.

FIG. 47—The crescent of bright green fields at the head of Coisco Bay, midway between Santa and Chimbote, framed by dark hills whose ridges and spurs are etched out in sharp relief by drifts of wind-blown sand, is a pleasant relief from the barren hills and sun-scorched desert which form most of the coast of Peru. Two marine terraces are clearly visible here. The wave-cut outer edge of the upper terrace which forms a wall-like border to the irrigated fields of the lower terrace is remarkably like that now being cut by the surf at the present shore line. The cliffs at the seaward end of the spur that extends across the center of the photograph seem as fresh as those against which the surf now breaks.

FIG. 48—The Chimbote Mountains, the end of the range of foothills of the Andes that limits the Santa Valley on the south, rise abruptly from the sea all the way from Coisco to Chimbote Bay except where an occasional embayment like that shown in the photograph permits the building of a bit of beach. Everywhere in these embayments signs of recent uplift are to be seen in the freshly wave-cut cliffs bordering the coastal plain. During much of the winter season the crests of the higher coastal hills are mantled with heavy fog like that which hides the summit of the promontory in the foreground. There is probably sufficient precipitation from it to support a sparse growth of shrubs and grasses.

FIG. 49—A view across one of the higher crests of the Chimbote Mountains to the lower hills and coastal plains behind them. The surf breaks directly against the foot of these mountains except for bits of wave-built coastal plain in an occasional embayment like that in the preceding photograph, and they are consequently largely bare of wind-blown sand as compared with the lower hills behind them which are masked almost to their tops with sand blown up from the low plains that border Chimbote Bay. The Chimbote Mountains rise over 1500 feet, and mist from the moisture-laden winds from the Pacific frequently veils their crests only to be dissipated when it reaches the lower hills.

Fig. 50—Part of the port of Chimbote on Chimbote Bay, the best harbor of the Peruvian coast—a landlocked bay seven miles long by three and a half miles wide. The port is now of little consequence, serving only the haciendas of the delta of the Santa River and, to some extent, the mining districts of the Callejón de Huailas, as the valley of the upper river between the Cordillera Blanca and the Cordillera Negra of the Andes is called. It will be an important port when projected extensions to the irrigation systems of the delta are completed and the railway, which now runs northward across the delta and up the river to a point eighty-six miles from the port, is completed.

FIG. 51—Samanco Bay lies south of Chimbote Bay, separated from it only by a low, lagoon-filled neck of land and like it is closed by high peninsulas at either end and a row of rocky islands across its mouth. Samanco, the port on the bay, is the shipping point for the valley of the Nepeña or Guambacho River. The river is small and seldom carries water to the sea, but during the excessively heavy rains of 1925 it flooded its valley and when it had subsided was found to have built up a wide delta that left the port and its 370-foot pier high and dry. A new port had to be established almost three miles farther north. The photograph shows the old port after the flood.

FIG. 52—The new port of Samanco established when the old port shown in Figure 51 was abandoned after the floods of 1925. The new port, like the old, is of minor importance and has no rail connection with the valley it serves. Sugar is the chief export, and some cotton is also shipped.

FIG. 53—A photograph of the new port of Samanco from the south showing the foothills of the Andes that border Samanco Bay. Two coastal terraces of marine origin can be seen in the photograph. The second row of buildings stands just back of the well defined cliff at the edge of the upper terrace. In the coves in the lower right corner of the photograph now lifted above the sea the wave-cut edges of the terraces and of the rocks that enclose the coves look as though the surf were still beating against them.

FIG. 54—In contrast to the low coastal plain bordering Chimbote Bay, on Samanco Bay, except at its extreme northern part, the foothills of the Andes come down to the sea, and there are only occasional bits of narrow coastal plain. On the other hand, whereas Chimbote Bay is deep close to the shore, the eastern part of Samanco Bay is shallow and dotted with islands; and at low tide wide stretches of beach are exposed from which sand is blown up into the gulleys between the spurs of the foothills that border the shore.

Fig. 55—A closer view of a section of Figure 54 showing the wind ripples in the sand that is blown up into the coastal hills during low tide. The tide was ebbing when this photograph was taken; but the beach, which is exposed at low tide, was still covered by shallow water beneath which a maze of tidal channels can be seen. The aerial photograph has been found to be of great service in the study of such underwater features.

FIG. 56—Clouds frequently form over the high hills (1000 to 1500 feet) that border Samanco Bay and precipitate sufficient moisture to support patches of sparse vegetation on their crests, as shown in the foreground of this photograph. Behind these coastal hills low irregular ranges of hills covered almost to their tops with wind-blown sand stretch away toward the foothills of the Cordillera Negra—the high range of the Andes that encloses the Callejón de Huailas, the valley of the upper Santa River, on the west.

FIG. 57—The fishing village of Los Chinos lies on a low coastal terrace at the head of a snug little cove a few miles south of Samanco Bay. Samanco Point, the headland that encloses Samanco Bay on the south, can be seen in the upper right corner of the photograph. Los Chinos, like many of these coastal settlements, has a small industry of salt-making by evaporation from sea water. The evaporating vats, here white with the finished product, lie along the edge of the lagoon at the front of the wave-cut cliff bordering the lower terrace back of the village.

FIG. 58—One of the most rugged and picturesque sections of the coast of Peru. From Los Chinos Cove (see Fig. 57) a narrow embayment, backed by rugged hills and dotted with rocky islands, extends southward for about five miles to Peña Negra, the high, dark promontory that forms the northern portal of Casma Bay. Tortuga Cove and Islands, the subject of this photograph, are at the southern end of this embayment. The dark slopes of Peña Negra show in the lower right corner of the photograph.

FIG. 59—The high headlands of bare, black rocks which form the portals of Casma Bay—Peña Negra in the north and Calvario Bluff (shown in the foreground of the photograph) on the south—afford good protection to shipping; and the horseshoe-shaped cove in the lee of Calvario Bluff, where the port of Casma is located, is a particularly snug anchorage. The port serves not only the irrigated valley of the Casma River but is also the chief port for the mining districts of the upper Santa River, a two or three days' journey by muleback across the Cordillera Negra. Cotton is its chief export with some rice and also wood and charcoal from the algarrobo forests just back of the port.

FIG. 60—The port of Casma from the north with the slopes of Calvario Bluff in the background, their edges clearly wave-cut where they border the coastal plain; and, in the foreground, the low lagoon-filled flood plain of the Casma River separated from the sea by a narrow wave-built sand barrier. The canal cut straight across the beach from the sea carries water to the rows of vats back of the settlement in which salt is produced by evaporation. These vats are shallow pits dug in the earth. The various tints shown in them in the photograph indicate various stages in the evaporation process—from greens and blues in the freshly filled vats to beautiful reds and pinks and finally dazzling white.

FIG. 61—Bulto Point and North Island at the northern end of Huarmey Bay, the next important harbor south of Casma Bay. North Island, white with guano, is a landmark for shipping entering the bay from the north. The absence of boats of any sort on the beach shows that this settlement is not a fishing village. The buildings appear to be temporary, open-front structures, and it is probable that the settlement is only a bathing resort for the town of Huarmey situated a little over a mile inland from this point.

FIG. 62—At the port of Huarmey, the port for the town of Huarmey, which is about two miles northeast in the valley of Huarmey River, the irrigated fields again come down to the shore. The Huarmey River approaches the shore in a wide, many-channeled bed but rarely reaches the sea except in seasons of unusual rainfall in the Cordillera Negra where it has its source. In normal seasons it ends in the long lagoon that follows the shore northward from the port for two miles just back of the wave-cut edge of the lower coastal terrace. The protection afforded the bay by Lagarto Head, the promontory in the foreground of the photograph, makes this one of the best anchorages of the coast.

FIG. 63—The port of Huarmey from the north with the slopes of Lagarto Head in the background and, in the foreground, the end of the lagoon with the Huarmey River entering from the left. The valley of the Huarmey River is small, and the port consequently is of minor importance with cotton as the chief export. The manufacture of salt from sea water is an industry at this port as at the port of Casma. In the photograph the vats appear to have just been emptied. Back of those now in use are others which have been filled with drifted sand and abandoned. At most of these ports, drifting sand piles up against outlying buildings and even invades the streets.

FIG. 64—Lagarto Head, the promontory that shelters Huarmey Bay on the south. The view is characteristic of much of the coast of Peru—irregular, barren, sun-scorched hills drifted with sand, their seaward edges cut to steep cliffs by the steady pounding of the surf.

FIG. 65—Seal Bay, on the south side of Lagarto Head, is one of the many beautiful little coves that indent the coast of Peru in its more rugged section between Salaverry and Cerro Azul. The hills surrounding it are completely desertic. There is not a sign of life in the sand which covers them to their tops. That the coast is not entirely rainless is shown by the systems of shallow gulleys in the sand. These gulleys may have been made by rains that occurred several years before the photograph was taken, since the sand which covers the hills seems very hard and shows no wind effects. These systems of gulleys made by the rare rains of the coast region frequently remain unchanged for years.

Fig. 66—La Fortaleza, one of the best preserved of the pre-colonial fortresses of Peru, is one of a group of eight hilltop defenses that are believed to have marked the southern limit of the kingdom of the Great Chimú. The less well-preserved remains of others can be seen in the background. Here it is said that one of the battles between the Great Chimú and the Inca invaders of his kingdom took place. The group of fortresses stands close to the sea in the midst of cultivated fields on the north side of the Fortaleza River. La Fortaleza consists of three terrace-like platforms enclosed by a high wall and approached by narrow passageways commanded by ramparts and watchtowers.

FIG. 67—The rugged coastal hills that border the lower valley of the Fortaleza River on the north. In the foreground is an alluvial fan filling the mouth of a narrow valley tributary to the main river. These fans of raw, infertile earth at the mouths of ravines between the hills that limit the flood plains of the rivers of the coastal region are a characteristic feature of all the coastal valleys.

FIG. 68—A view from above of the irregular range of coastal hills that borders the valley of the Fortaleza River on the north. In a flight by airplane along the coast the greater part of the journey is over landscape like this. The widely-separated river valleys with their rich green fields are only occasional incidents of the trip. They constitute not more than three per cent of the whole coastal region.

FIG. 69—Sugar is now the most important agricultural product of Peru, the value of the sugar exported being now more than thirty per cent of that of the country's total exports. The greater part of the sugar is produced on large estates on many of which modern methods of cultivation and extraction have been introduced. One of the largest and most efficiently managed of these is the Paramonga estate in the valley of the Pativilca River, now controlled by W. R. Grace and Co. The photograph shows the administrative center of the estate built on an erosion remnant above the irrigable level of the valley with the sugar mills and the railway to the port of Supé (see Fig. 1) in the foreground.

FIG. 70—Carquin Bay and Point from the north with the town of Carquin on the edge of the irrigated delta of the Huaura River. The river rises in the main cordillera of the Andes and consequently carries water to the sea throughout the year. Carquin Bay would be a most convenient shipping point for the plantations of the Huaura Valley; but it is useless as a harbor on account of the particularly heavy swell that prevails there at all times, and the products of the valley are shipped from the port of Huacho (see Fig. 8) on the next embayment about two and a half miles farther south. The town is a fishing village and bathing resort.

FIG. 71—Bajas Point, the tip of the high Salinas Promontory which encloses Salinas Bay, the next harbor south of Huacho (see Fig. 8) on the south. The scene is typical of much of that section of the coast of Perú between Salaverry and Cerro Azul where the foothills of the Andes come down to the shore and the surf breaks directly against their base. For long distances in this section of the coast the only flat land visible from the sea is the deltas built up by the occasional streams which carry their water to the sea during at least a part of the year. Salinas Promontory rises so abruptly from the sea that there is not even a footpath around its seaward side.

Fig. 72—Toma-Calla Point at the northern end of Ancón Bay is a rocky spur of Cerro Arena, a high coastal hill rising directly from the sea. Its white cover of guano, standing out in sharp contrast to the dark wave-cut cliffs at its base, makes it a good landmark for ships entering the bay from the north. Here, as at the Salinas Promontory, there is not even room for a footpath along the shore. The railway from Lima to Huacho by way of Ancón follows a depression back of Cerro Arena.

FIG. 73—Between Chancay and Ancón Bay coastal hills—their flanks buried deep with sand, their feet cut to steep cliffs and indented with little coves—rise directly from the sea and form a high wall shutting off all view of the land behind them.

FIG. 74—A photograph of the tops of the hills back of Ancón with the foothills of the Andes in the background and, in the foreground, the sand dunes of which a closer view is shown in Figure 77. These fields of dunes are a characteristic feature of the coastal region.

FIG. 75—Barren, sand-covered hills rising to nearly 3000 feet form the background for the dazzling white houses and tree-lined streets of Ancón. In pre-colonial days the vicinity of the bay was evidently well populated. The coastal plain and the lower slopes of the hills contain many ruins and large cemeteries, but today only uninhabited desert surrounds the town. There are no streams entering the bay, and drinking water must be brought by rail from Lima. The principal training base of the Peruvian Naval Air Service is located at Ancón. Its buildings can be seen at the left end of the town. There Lieutenant Johnson had his laboratory, in which the photographs reproduced in this volume were printed.

FIG. 76—Ancón is located on one of the best harbors of the Peruvian coast. Ships can anchor in five fathoms of water close to the end of the piers. But the town is of little importance as a shipping point. Around it for miles stretch sandy desert and barren hills. The nearest irrigated valley, the valley of the Chillón River (see map, Fig. 4), exports its products through the more easily accessible port of Callao. Ancón has long been a popular bathing resort for the city of Lima, with which it is connected by rail. In the War of the Pacific between Peru and Chile the bay was used by the Chilean fleet as a base for its attack on Callao. At Ancón the treaty which ended the war was signed.

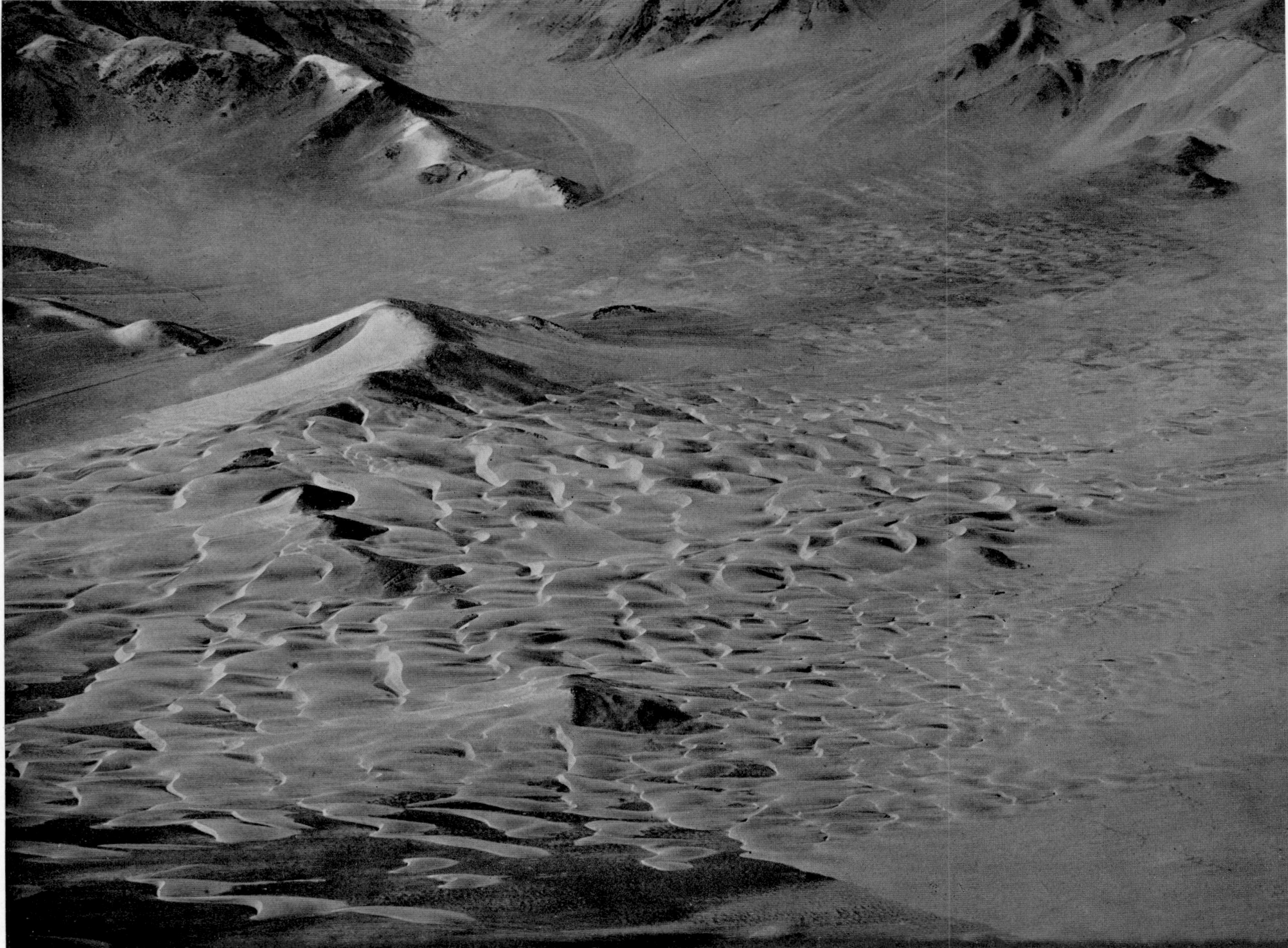

FIG. 77—Sand dunes on the lower slopes of the hills back of Ancón. Note the perfect crescentic form of the two isolated dunes in the left foreground. Compare their regular form—the result of regular winds—with the fantastic shapes of those shown in Figure 106.

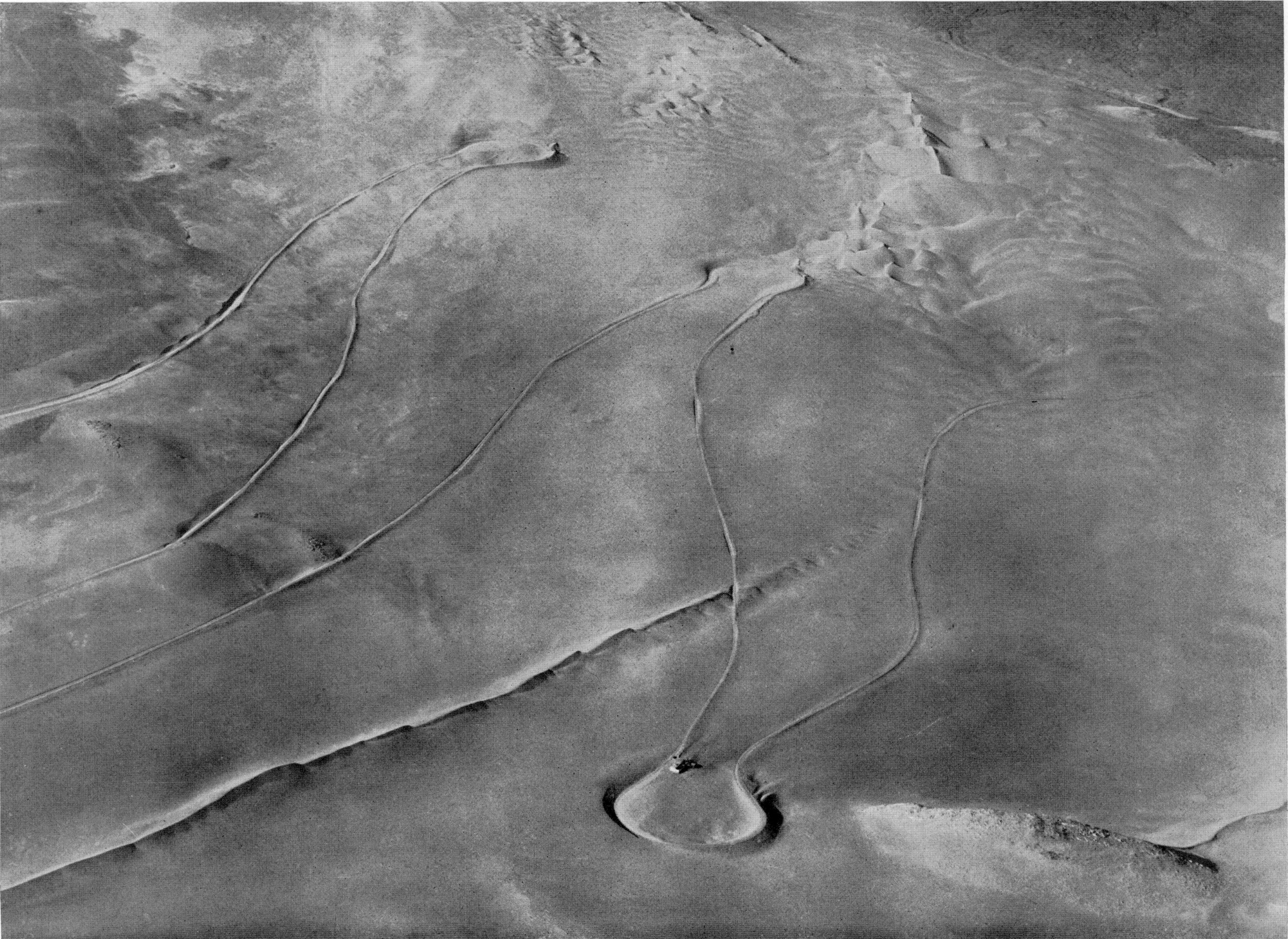

Fig. 78—The railway between Ancón and Huacho winding up through the deep sand that covers the hills north of Ancón. Note the sharp crests at the front of the dunes in the background. The keeping of the tracks clear of sand must be a considerable item in the upkeep of the railway. The hairpin curves of this railway are quite unnecessary. They were devised by the contractors to increase the construction mileage.

FIG. 79—One of the guano islands off the coast of Peru near Ancón.

FIG. 80—Seaplanes in flight along the coast between Ancón and Callao.

FIG. 81—Hills between Ancón and Lima. The curious mottled effect on the hill slopes is apparently caused by light-colored sand being blown up into the ravines and gulleys in the loose, easily-eroded surface of these hills. In the background is a broad alluvial fan now dry but still marked by numerous braided watercourses. The stream bed in the foreground is also dry, but there appears to be vegetation on the islands among its many stone-strewn channels. In the lower right corner of the photograph are two enclosures which look like the earthen threshing floors found everywhere in Peru where grain is raised. On them grain is still threshed with flails or tramped out by cattle or mules.

FIG. 82—The bare hills that border the Rimac Valley on the north (see also Fig. 5), looking, with their steep slopes and sharp crests, like models cut in stone. Their chiseled appearance is due to the fact that under the infrequent and scanty rains of the coastal region there is little accumulation of waste except in the deeper ravines. In the foreground at the left an alluvial fan meets the irrigated fields of the delta of the Rimac River. Note that this fan has had no important effect on the character of the edge of the delta because it is built up so much more slowly than is the flood plain of the glacier-fed Rimac. The flood plain seems to be slowly burying the spurs and fans which border it.

FIG. 83—Another view of the tops of the range of hills shown in Figure 82.

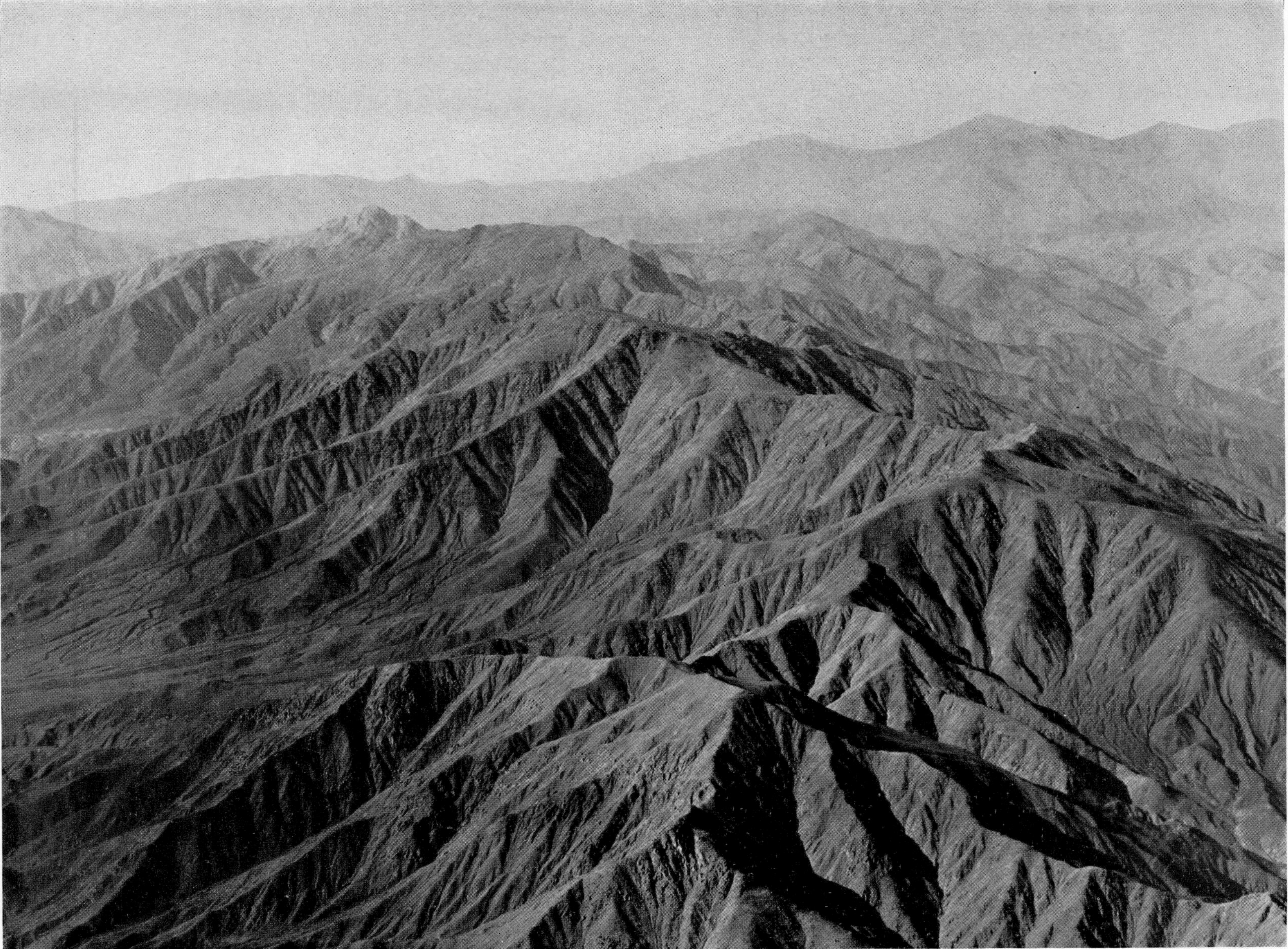

FIG. 84—The tops of the hills north of the Rimac Valley with the foothills of the Andes in the background.

FIG. 85—The colonial section of the city of Lima with the Plaza de Armas and the cathedral in the center of the photograph. The Rimac River cuts diagonally across the left corner of the photograph. Note the bull ring at the upper left edge of the built-up section at the left of the river. Lima is situated at the inner edge of the wide delta of the Rimac River (see map, Fig. 4). The river emerges from its narrow valley through the foothills of the Andes just east of the city. The fog drifting in from the left is characteristic. Through some peculiarity of its physiographic setting Lima seems to lie in a sort of fog pocket; and frequently during the winter the sun is hidden from the city for weeks at a time.

FIG. 86—Part of the more modern section of Lima which has been developed south of the limits of the colonial section. In the center is the Hipodromo Santa Beatriz, used for athletic sports. The avenue that leads diagonally out of the city to the right from the circular Plaza Dos de Mayo is the new concrete road to Magdalena, a near-by seaside suburb; while the wider avenue leading out of this plaza toward the lower left corner of the photograph is the new Boulevard Alfonso Ugarte which connects it with the Plaza Bolognesi shown in the lower right corner of Figure 85. The large park at the left of the Plaza Dos de Mayo is the Zoölogical Gardens.

FIG. 87—A closer view of a section of Figure 86, taken from an altitude of 700 feet and looking south toward the seaside suburbs of Miraflores and Chorrillos which can be seen at the very upper edge of the photograph. In the foreground are the Zoölogical Gardens with the track for dog-racing just above them. Above this track to the left is the football stadium.

FIG. 88—The inner edge of the delta of the Rimac River with the foothills of the Andes in the background and, in the foreground, the eastern end of the colonial section of Lima. The river—a broad, braided stream—can be seen emerging from its narrow flood plain between the foothills and crossing diagonally toward the right of the photograph, where it enters the city under the old bridge leading to the bull ring. The Central Railway, one of the world's outstanding achievements in railway engineering, follows the Rimac River to its source in glacier-fed lakes in the main cordillera on its way to Oroya, reaching in the tunnel by which it crosses the cordillera an altitude of 15,665 feet.

FIG. 89—Airplanes in flight along the edge of the irrigated fields of the Rimac delta.

FIG. 90—The Las Palmas Airport near Lima.

FIG. 91—One of the poorer outlying sections of Lima built around one of the great pre-colonial burial mounds, many of which are to be found on the Rimac delta. These burial mounds contain thousands of mummified bodies, each enclosed in little compartments walled with mud bricks. Most of them have been partly excavated. The new Avenida del Progreso, the fine concrete road that connects Lima with Callao, cuts directly through one of the largest of them, and many hundreds of bodies were disinterred during the process of excavating the roadway.

Fig. 92—Part of the harbor front and town of Callao with the old mole and the new breakwater. The mole, part of which dates from 1865, is operated by a French company and is popularly known as the "French mole." It is equipped with cranes and railways which connect all parts of it with the shore and has accommodations for four steamers of three hatchways each, eleven sailing vessels of two hatchways each, and seven barges. About forty per cent of the ships entering Callao harbor use the mole. These include all sailing vessels, all lumber carriers, and certain other ships that have no regular sailing schedule. Fast steamers on regular schedule load and unload at anchor as at other ports.

FIG. 93—The new piers immediately north of the French mole, now under construction as a part of the new port improvement project known as the Leguia Terminal. The port of Callao is one of the oldest on the west coast, having been founded in 1537, two years after the founding of Lima. The town is now the second city of Peru in size, its present population being between fifty and sixty thousand. A large number of men are employed in loading and unloading operations on the piers, and in addition a considerable portion of the population is employed in the numerous factories now located in the town. The population of the town is largely of the working class.

FIG. 94—A Grace Line steamer at anchor in Callao harbor unloading freight into launches for transfer to the piers. Callao is the port not only for the irrigated lands of the valleys of the Rimac and Chillón rivers but also for the mines of the Cerro de Pasco and Huancavelica districts. Sugar is the chief export from the irrigated valleys, with cotton a close second. Copper and silver are the principal exports from the mines of the Andes. Over ten million dollars' worth of copper is shipped annually from the Cerro de Pasco region alone.

FIG. 95—La Punta, the low point of land extending out into the sea beyond Callao which with San Lorenzo Island protects the harbor of Callao on the south. La Punta is now of considerable importance as a fashionable bathing and health resort and has a population of about twelve hundred, mainly of the well-to-do class. There also is located the Peruvian Naval Academy.

FIG. 96—One of the higher crests of San Lorenzo, a large, rocky island, rising to an altitude of over 1200 feet toward its northern end, which protects Callao Bay on the south (see map, Fig. 4). From La Punta, shown in the preceding photograph, a long spit extending out toward the island assists in protecting the bay from the heavy swell that rolls up at times from the south. The narrow passage between the end of the spit and the island is at no point more than five fathoms deep and is exceptionally rough. Ships entering Callao Bay from the south round the northern end of San Lorenzo. The government arsenal and submarine base are located on the island.

FIG. 97—Miraflores, a bathing resort and fashionable residential suburb of Lima (see map, Fig. 4). The town consists largely of fine residences set in beautiful gardens. Note the absence of the monotonous rows of low houses that line the streets of the poorer class of seaside towns. Miraflores is within easy access of Lima by railway, electric tramway, and motor road.

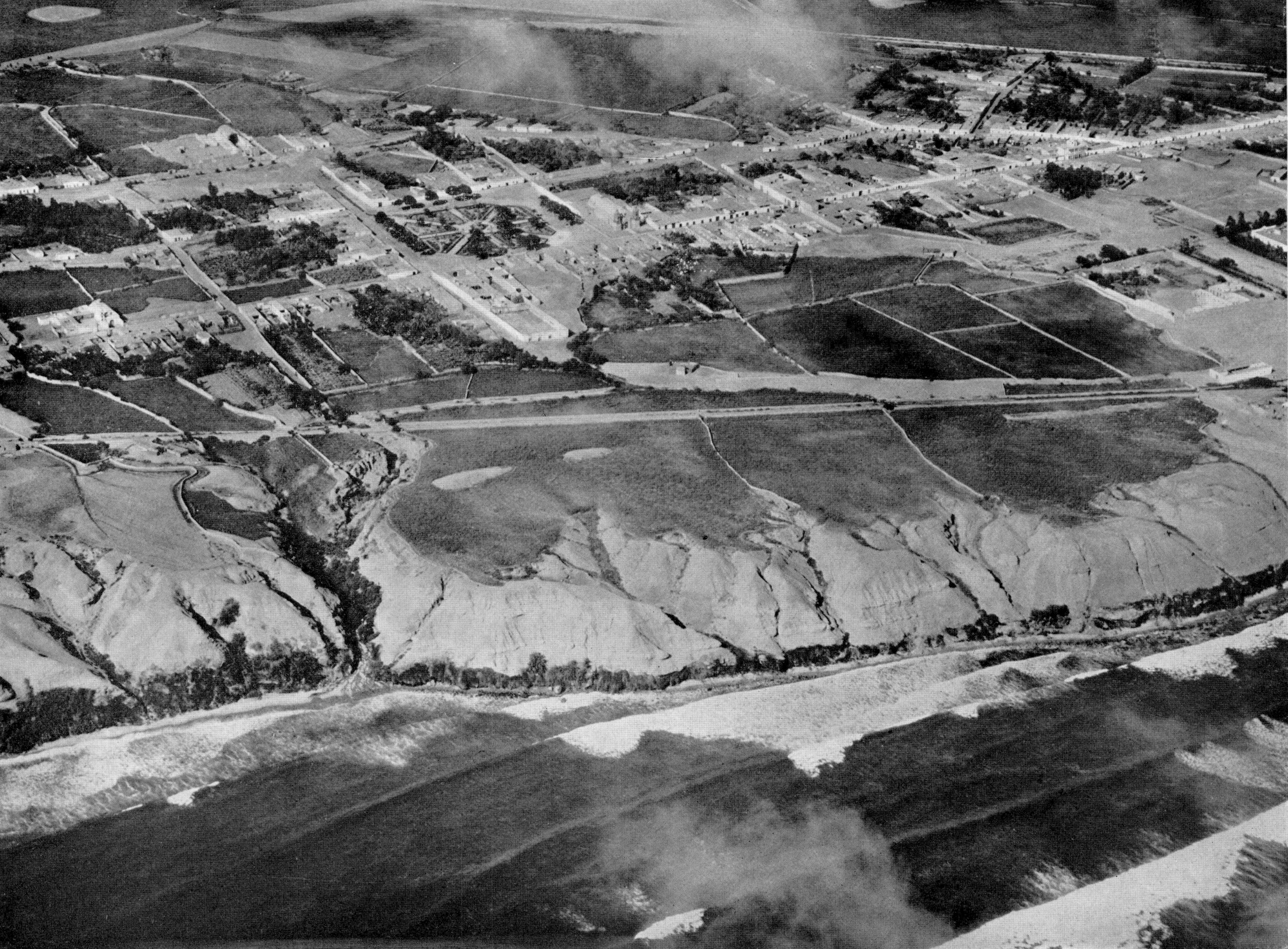

FIG. 98—Barranco, another seaside residential suburb of Lima two miles south of Miraflores, so called from the Spanish term for the high clay cliffs that border the shore in front of the town. The town is entirely a development of the last fifty years and consists largely of small estates noted for their fine houses and gardens. All these seaside suburbs are connected with Lima by railway, tramway, and motor road.

FIG. 99—Chorrillos, a popular bathing resort for wealthy citizens of Lima, lies south of Barranco and is practically continuous with it. The rocky point at the right of the town is a spur from the Morro Solar, a cluster of hills rising directly from the plain to an altitude of 890 feet, and is known as the Salto del Fraile. The bathing beach is on a little bay south of this point. The road from the town to the beach can be seen winding up the hill at the right of the town and crossing it by means of a short tunnel.

FIG. 100—Chilca Bay, about thirty-five miles south of Callao, is an exceptionally safe harbor (note the absence of heavy surf in the photograph) but is too small for large steamers. Chilca Island, shown in the left foreground of the photograph separated from the mainland by a narrow channel, protects the bay on the south. The town of Chilca lies inland about three miles southeast of the port in the valley of the Chilca River. The valley is small, and shipping at the port is of no great importance. The little settlement on the cove at the right of the photograph is Pucusana, a popular bathing beach of the region. A branch road suitable for automobiles connects it with the main road from Lima to Iça.

FIG. 101—Asia Island, a large guano island close to the mainland about twenty miles south of Chilca. The island, although almost completely covered with guano, appears to be deserted of birds except for two small clusters. Dr. Robert C. Murphy, in his book "Bird Islands of Peru," reports that during October and November of 1919 vultures, gulls, and condors destroyed thousands of nests on this island. It is possible that the destruction has continued until only these two small groups of birds are left.

FIG. 102—Another view of Asia Island. Dr. Murphy describes this guano-covered island with its deep ravines as looking like a frosted cake from which portions have been cut out. The island is one of the most unhealthful spots on the Peruvian coast. Mosquitos from the low coastal plain of the near-by mainland swarm over it and infect the guano extractors with malaria. The island is also noted for its extraordinarily large numbers of vampire bats. They attack animals and even poultry so that none can be kept on the island.

FIG. 103—Cerro Azul, eighty miles south of Callao, lies on a little bay slightly protected on the south by a small, hilly point known as Fraile Point and is the port for the sugar and cotton plantations of the valley of the Cañete River. The river, which empties into the sea eight miles south of the port, carries water to the sea throughout the year. Its wide delta comes down to the shore and was the site of some of the earliest sugar plantations in Peru. In 1923 the government completed there the first of its large irrigation projects, adding 20,000 acres of cultivable land to the valley. The 35-kilometer railway from the valley to the port is one of the oldest in Peru, the first ten kilometers dating from 1867.

Fig. 104—A view of the lower end of Cerro Azul Bay across Cerro Azul (blue hill), so called from plants of the genus *Tillandsia* which formerly covered it. These coastal hills were terraced and cultivated to their tops in pre-colonial times; and Cerro Sentinella, the hill shown at the end of the point in Figure 103, had on its summit one of the finest and most elaborate of the Inca fortresses. For more than a hundred and fifty years the early viceroys preserved it as an example of Inca architecture, but it was finally largely demolished and the stones used to rebuild the breakwater at Callao destroyed in the earthquake of 1687. On Cerro Azul are the remains of fortifications erected during the War of the Pacific.

Fig. 105—The old wooden pier at Cerro Azul with the settlement of stevedores and boatmen at its head. The new pier of steel and concrete shown in Figure 103 is of recent construction. The port is growing steadily in importance as new lands are brought under cultivation in the Cañete Valley and has now a population of about four hundred. (For discussion of the development of new lands in the coastal valleys see page 14.)

FIG. 106—Sand-covered hills back of the port of Cerro Azul with the edge of the irrigated fields of the valley and the railway connecting the estates and towns of the valley with the port in the foreground. The dunes at Cerro Azul (see Fig. 104) show no such regularity of form as those seen in the photographs taken farther north. They have a most fantastic irregularity, as though the winds that form them were very irregular in direction and force. Compare them with the regular crescentic dunes at Ancón shown in Figure 77.

FIG. 107—The high, steep cliffs at the edge of the irrigated coastal plain north of Pisco.

FIG. 108—The delta at the mouth of the Pisco River, the only one of its kind known on the coast of Peru. Elsewhere the deltas either do not reach the shore or, where they do reach the shore, end in perpendicular wave-cut cliffs.

FIG. 109—The port of Pisco, port for the valleys of the Pisco and Iça rivers with which it is connected by rail. The *pueblo* of Pisco (see Fig. 110) is about a mile inland and is connected with the port by an electric tramway. The harbor, Pisco Bay, is slightly protected on the south by Paracas Peninsula and on the west by the Chincha and Ballestas guano island groups and other small groups of islands; but shipping at the port is much handicapped by wind and swell, particularly by a strong southerly breeze which usually begins in the forenoon and continues with increasing intensity until late afternoon, frequently halting all shipping operations. The port is, however, the most important between Callao and Mollendo.

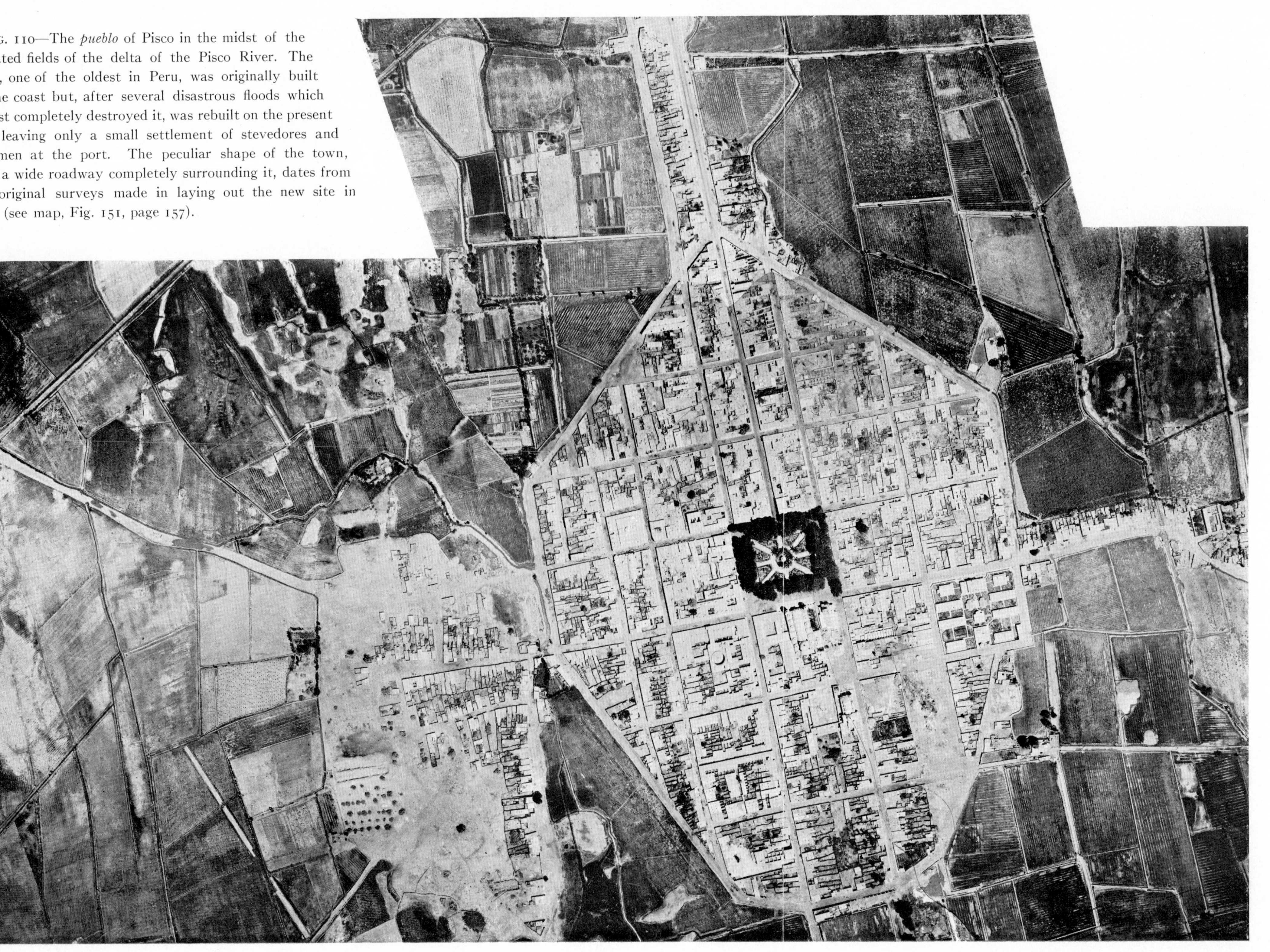

FIG. 110—The *pueblo* of Pisco in the midst of the irrigated fields of the delta of the Pisco River. The town, one of the oldest in Peru, was originally built on the coast but, after several disastrous floods which almost completely destroyed it, was rebuilt on the present site, leaving only a small settlement of stevedores and boatmen at the port. The peculiar shape of the town, with a wide roadway completely surrounding it, dates from the original surveys made in laying out the new site in 1713 (see map, Fig. 151, page 157).

FIG. 111—San Andres, a fishing village about a mile south of the port of Pisco.

Fig. 112—A temporary station of the Peruvian Naval Air Service on the beach on the inner edge of Paracas Peninsula, the point of land that encloses Pisco Bay on the south. In the background are the hills, rising to elevations of over six hundred feet, that form the northern end of the peninsula. Paracas Peninsula is formed by the northern extremity of the broken ranges of coastal hills by which the Coast Range is continued north of the Ocoña River (see map, Fig. 2). South of the Ocoña River is the true Coast Range, a range of old mountains several thousand feet high which extends southward beyond the Chilean border (see Figs. 116 to 119).

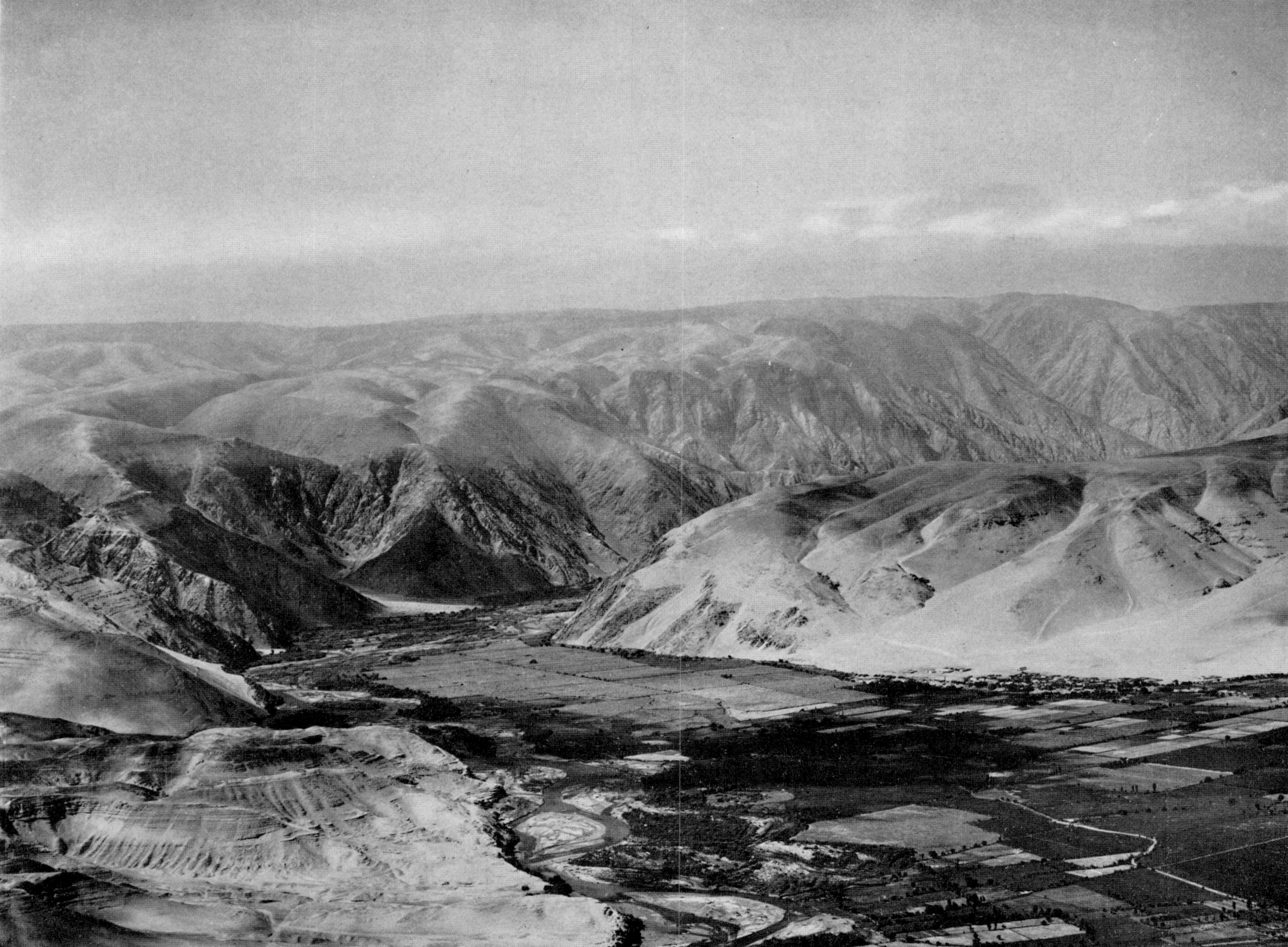

Fig. 113—The lower Camaná or Majes Valley with the Coast Range in the foreground, the lofty plateau of the Andes seen dimly through the cloud banks in the background, and the high desert pampas between them. The flat-floored, steep-walled valley of the Camaná or Majes River swings in from the right, describing a great curve as it cuts through the Coast Range. In its passage through the Coast Range and in the broader valley open to the sea the river flows on the surface of the alluvial fill of the valley in a many-channeled and oft-changing bed. The older, abandoned channels are marked by growths of trees and shrubs. The town of Camaná is seen at the right.

FIG. 114—Camaná, the chief town of the Camaná Valley, appears in Figure 113 to lie at the edge of the sand-covered seaward-facing slopes of the Coast Range; but in this photograph it is seen to be in the midst of the irrigated fields of the valley floor. The town lies three miles inland from the mouth of the Camaná River but, owing to the physiographic character of the coast at the mouth of the river (see note 3, page 158), has no port there. The only outlet for the products of the valley is by trail along the shore twenty-seven miles to Quilca, a minor port at the mouth of the Vitor River (see map, Fig. 17), and thence by small boats to Mollendo.

Fig. 115—A village in the lower Camaná Valley. The Camaná or Majes River carries an abundance of water for the irrigation of the valley; but the lack of a convenient port has hindered the development of the valley, and much of it lacks an efficient system of water supply and control. Many of the fields near this village appear to be either without sufficient water or badly leached because of poor drainage.

FIG. 116—The summit and seaward-facing slopes of the Coast Range south of the Camaná Valley with the upper coastal terrace (see notes, Figs. 18 and 19) abutting sharply against them at the left of the photograph and, in the left background, the sea and the wave-cut cliffs at the edge of the lower terrace. Clouds form frequently over the Coast Range and even over the upper terrace, precipitating sufficient moisture on the upper slopes of the range to support a sparse growth of grass and shrubs and to feed a few small streams that water a bit of cultivated land here and there at the base of the range. It is largely due to these streams that the upper coastal terrace is so much more dissected than the lower.

FIG. 117—A view across the summit of the Coast Range and the high desert *pampas* which lie between it and the plateau of the Andes. The photograph shows particularly well the character of these two features of the coastal region of southern Peru—the gentle slopes of the old mountains that form the Coast Range and the monotonous surface of the *pampas*, broken only by fields of dunes or irregular drifts of sand and deposits of *tierra blanca*—the patches of white earth shown in the photograph (see p. 20).

Fig. 118—The high desert pampas back of the Coast Range between Camaná and Mollendo with the Andes in the background (a bit of the snow-capped Nudo de Ampato shows at the extreme right) and, in the foreground, one of the deep, transverse valleys that divide the high plains between the Coast Range and the Andes into so-called "pampas," each of which has a separate name. In the foreground at the left of the river is the edge of the Pampa de Sihuas, while the Pampa de Vitor fills the greater part of the photograph. (For location see map, Fig. 17.)

FIG. 119—A stream from the Andes, which can be seen dimly in the background of the photograph, winds in a deep, narrow canyon across the high desert Pampa de Sihuas and cuts through the Coast Range on its way to the sea. (For a description of these pampas, see page 20.) Patches of tough grass fill the moist hollows left when the broad, wet-season river subsided to its present narrow, dry-season channel.

FIG. 120—The port of Mollendo. (See also Fig. 18.) This is one of the roughest sections of the west coast, and Mollendo has the heaviest surf of all the Peruvian ports—so heavy as to prevent the construction of piers as at the other ports. A slip, seen at the right end of the town in the photograph, has been made by building a breakwater out over a group of rocks close to the shore. In this slip the launches that transfer cargoes to and from ships at anchor out beyond the surf are loaded and unloaded. Even in the slip the surf is so heavy that cattle, of which considerable numbers are shipped from this port, must be swung into the launches by means of cranes.

FIG. 121—A closer view of Mollendo. In the right foreground is the slip in which cargo and passengers are transferred by cranes to and from the launches and small boats that ply between the slip and steamers anchored out beyond the surf. Note the heavy surf breaking at the inner end of the slip. At the end of the slip are the yards and freight sheds of the Southern Railway of Peru, which connects the port with Lake Titicaca and Cuzco by way of Arequipa. The port serves the southern interior provinces of Peru as far north as Cuzco and was until recently second only to Callao in volume of foreign trade. Now it is surpassed in volume of exports by Talara, the port for the northern oil fields.

FIG. 122—El Misti Volcano from the northeast. The photograph was taken from a point almost directly opposite that from which Figure 21 was taken. Note the smoothness of the east side of the cone and its lack of snow as compared with the deeply eroded flanks and snow-capped summit of the west side. It appears from these two photographs that the greater part of the precipitation on El Misti comes from the Pacific. Even on the west side, however, the snow is temporary only and disappears during at least a short period of most years. The snows of the wet season extend down to 16,000 feet (3000 feet below the summit) and, in exceptional years, to 14,000 feet.

FIG. 123—The summit of El Misti from the southeast with the snow-capped Nevado de Chachani (see map, Fig. 17, and Figs. 132 and 133) back of the volcano at the left and a long line of snow crests in the background. The dividing line between the snow fields and deeply-eroded slope of the more rainy western side of the summit of El Misti and the drier eastern side with practically no snow and relatively little erosion is clearly shown in this photograph.

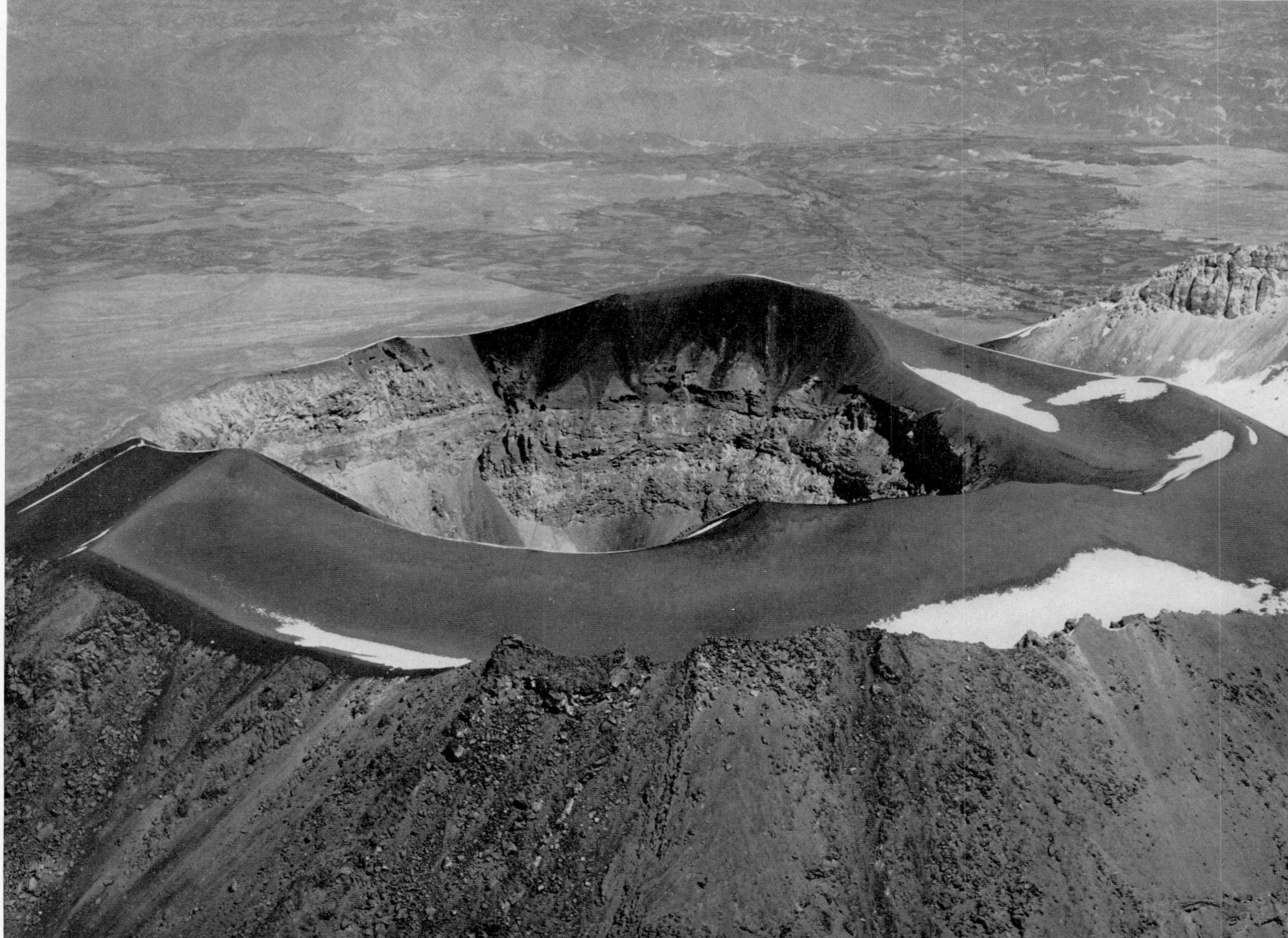

FIG. 124—The crater of El Misti from the northeast with Arequipa and the Chili Valley in the background. The volcano has a double crater, the rim of the newer crater—as can be seen in the foreground of the photograph—fitting entirely within the partly destroyed rim of the older crater. The snow patches in the foreground are in the outer slopes of the rim of the inner crater. The remarkably smooth rim of the inner crater appears deep blue from the air with the interior of the crater a sulphurous yellow-green. This inner rim must be extremely hard to have resisted erosion for so many centuries; there having been no eruption of the volcano since the Conquest.

FIG. 125—The interior of the crater of El Misti from the north, with the fields of lava shown in Figures 126 and 127 in the background. At the left is the only section of the otherwise perfectly preserved rim of the crater that has broken away in the centuries that have passed since the cone was built. There are exposed the broken edges of layers of lava parallel to the outer slope of the cone. Although the volcano has not been in action in historical times, columns of smoke are frequently seen rising from it. In the photograph smoke can be seen in the foreground just inside the rim of the crater. (For further description and a sketch of the two craters see note 4, page 158.)

Fig. 126—Erosion effects in the lava fields at the base of El Misti.

FIG. 127—A continuation of the lava fields shown in Figure 126.

FIG. 128—A photograph from the southeast of the Arequipa Airport on an old lava flow at the base of El Misti Volcano. The port is used by the commercial planes of the Faucett Aviation Company and the Pan American-Grace Airways as one of their regular stops. Note on the surface of the lava field at the left the braided bed, dry when the photograph was taken, of a stream from the volcano.

Fig. 129—A well glaciated volcanic peak a few miles east of El Misti displaying remarkably fresh-looking features of glacial erosion. The three parallel cirques, now apparently free of glaciers, have been cut back by the ice and snow that formerly occupied them until the walls that separate them have been worn to narrow ridges. Shallow cols have been developed by the intersection of the two cirques farthest to the left with cirques on the opposite side of the crest. The glacial troughs extending down the slope from these cirques have the staircase form characteristic of the beds of mountain glaciers from which the glaciers have retreated before their beds reached a mature state of glaciation.

FIG. 130—A photograph from the north of Nevado de Pichu-Pichu, a range of partially destroyed volcanic peaks, about twelve miles southeast of El Misti. On Pichu-Pichu, as on El Misti, the heavier precipitation appears to be from the west. The eastern slopes have retained their conical form to a remarkable degree, while the west side has been greatly modified by the action of ice and snow. The crest in the foreground glaciated only on its western side is particularly striking. The glacial trough in the foreground, in which a stream is seen flowing down from a snow field at the back of a large cirque, exhibits the familiar forms of glacial erosion—lateral and terminal moraines and glacial pockets.

FIG. 131—The Pampa de Salinas, a basin without outlet enclosed by a group of volcanic peaks immediately east of Pichu-Pichu. The basin formerly contained a lake but is now virtually a salar, with only a small pond of water during the wet season, the salt beds of which consist largely of boronatrocalcite (ulexite), the chief source of borax, and, from their position and their impermeable character are believed to be derived from boric exhalations from the surrounding volcanoes that penetrated to the waters of the old lake from below. The beds are worked now to some extent; but the only outlet for the product is by muleback to Arequipa, and the output is consequently small.

FIG. 132—The south side of the Nevado de Chachani—the remains of an old volcano sculptured to a maze of serrate ridges and sharp peaks by the prolonged action of ice and snow which rises above the level of the plateau of the Andes northwest of El Misti (see map, Fig. 17). The glaciers have now disappeared from Chachani, but erosion is continued by the process of nivation. The mountain bears large snow fields during the wet season, the upper portions of which are permanent, for Chachani rises to nearly 20,000 feet, or almost a thousand feet above the level of perpetual snow—about 19,000 feet above sea level in this section of the Andes.

FIG. 133—The southwest end of the Nevado de Chachani. Chachani is scalloped by deep cirques from which the glaciers have now disappeared (note the large cirque at the left with a snow-fed stream flowing from it) and is surrounded by the characteristic features of mountain glaciation—lateral and terminal moraines, U-shaped glacial troughs, hanging valleys. Around it on all sides spreads the mature, gently-molded surface of the plateau summit. The Indian shepherds pasture their flocks of sheep and alpacas here well up toward the edge of the snow. Note the numerous trails that cross the foreground of the photograph and the shepherd's hut close to the brook at the left between the two main trails.

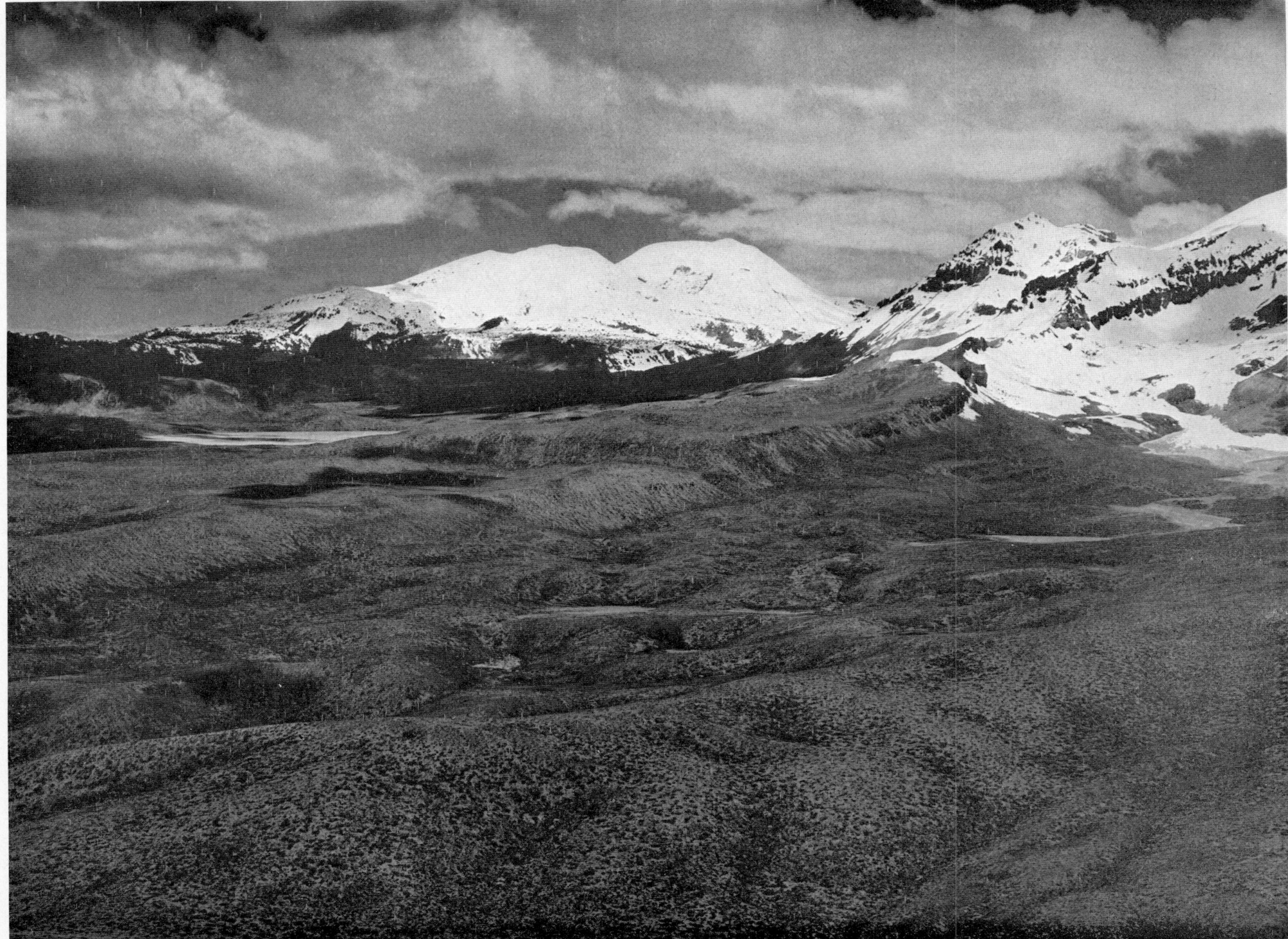

FIG. 134—The Nudo de Ampato (20,860 feet high), the highest of the old volcanoes which stand on the western edge of the plateau of the Andes in the vicinity of Arequipa, overlooks the deep gorge of the Colca River (see map, Fig. 17, and Figs. 23 to 28) and is the only one of the volcanic mountains shown in these aerial photographs which still bears remnants of its once great glaciers. Note the two large lateral moraines in the foreground of the photograph with a glacial stream winding down the shallow glacial trough between them. Clumps of vegetation, probably *tola* bushes and *ichu* grass, cover the surface of the plateau summit. Here the shepherds of the Colca Valley pasture their flocks.

FIG. 135—The Nudo de Ampato with the gently-molded, waste-covered surface of the plateau summit at its base and, in the foreground, the edge of the deep gorge of the Colca River. The glacial stream seen at the left of the center of this photograph is the stream shown at the right of Figure 134. Note the trail leading across the photograph just above the edge of the gorge. The camera has caught the physiographic features which predominate in this section of the Andes—wide stretches of high-level, well-graded, mature slopes with the snow-capped remnants of old volcanoes deeply eroded by the action of ice and snow rising above them and deep canyons falling away thousands of feet below them.

Fig. 136—Another view of the Nudo de Ampato showing its extensive snow fields. The two large cirques at the right of the photograph appear to be still occupied by glaciers. This is the only one of the old volcanoes of the Arequipa region known to have glaciers.

FIG. 137—The valley of the Palca or Tarma River near San Ramón (see Fig. 30).

FIG. 138—A continuation of Figure 137. The white roadway which follows the river—now dropping down to a narrow *playa* close to the edge of the river, now rising high above the river as it seeks the best of a precarious foothold—is the motor road from Oroya to La Merced—the only road passable for wheeled vehicles leading down from the plateau into the eastern valleys of the Andes. The only clearings in this section of the valley appear to be on a narrow *playa* here and there and on alluvial fans at the mouths of streams tributary to the main valley. Sugar cane is the principal crop on these clearings. From it alcohol is made for export to the plateau. (For a description of the region see page 31.)

Fig. 139—Forest-clad hills on the eastern border of the Andes near San Ramón.

FIG. 140—There is an abundance of rainfall in the eastern foothills of the Andes. In many of the valleys, however, evaporation on the northern and northwestern slopes, under the intense heat of the afternoon sun, is so rapid that the soil cannot retain sufficient moisture for tree growth, and only the shady ravines and slopes are forested (see Fig. 30); but in this photograph the hills are completely covered with dense forest.

FIG. 141—The Santa Clara coffee plantation in the Chanchamayo Valley. Coffee-raising is one of the chief industries of the valleys, and the bulk of the coffee used in Lima and central Peru is produced there. Note the large drying-floors in the photograph.

FIG. 142—The Naranjal coffee plantation—one of the most prosperous plantations of the Chanchamayo Valley located on a broad alluvial fan built by a stream tributary to the main river of the valley. The road which winds in from the left crossing the river by a narrow suspension bridge is the motor road from Oroya to San Ramón. On it motor trucks carry the products of the hacienda to the railway at Oroya.

FIG. 143—Another coffee plantation in the Chanchamayo Valley. On most of these coffee plantations a variety of food crops is also cultivated. Note the cattle in front of the long low buildings at the right of the manager's house and the drying floors and, in the left lower corner of the photograph, the rows of banana trees. The tropical fruits of this valley are considered among the finest produced in Peru.

FIG. 144—The headquarters of the Perené Colony on the Perené River about nine miles north of La Merced (see map, Fig. 29). The colony is owned and operated by the Peruvian Corporation, an English company formed in London in 1890 to take over from the government the principal railways of Peru in return for the cancellation of that portion of the national debt owed to British bondholders. A grant of 50,000 hectares of land on the Perené River for colonization purposes was included in the agreement of 1890. The colony is still largely in the experimental stage, although about 4000 hectares are now under cultivation. Coffee is the chief crop, but tropical fruits and other products are also grown.

FIG. 145—Forest-clad hills near the Perené River. It is over these hills that the old Pichis Trail leads from La Merced to Puerto Bermudez on the Pichis River on the land-and-water route from La Merced to Iquitos. Now seaplanes of the Peruvian Naval Air Service cover the same route and have shortened to one or two days the journey which by land and water takes nineteen days at least.

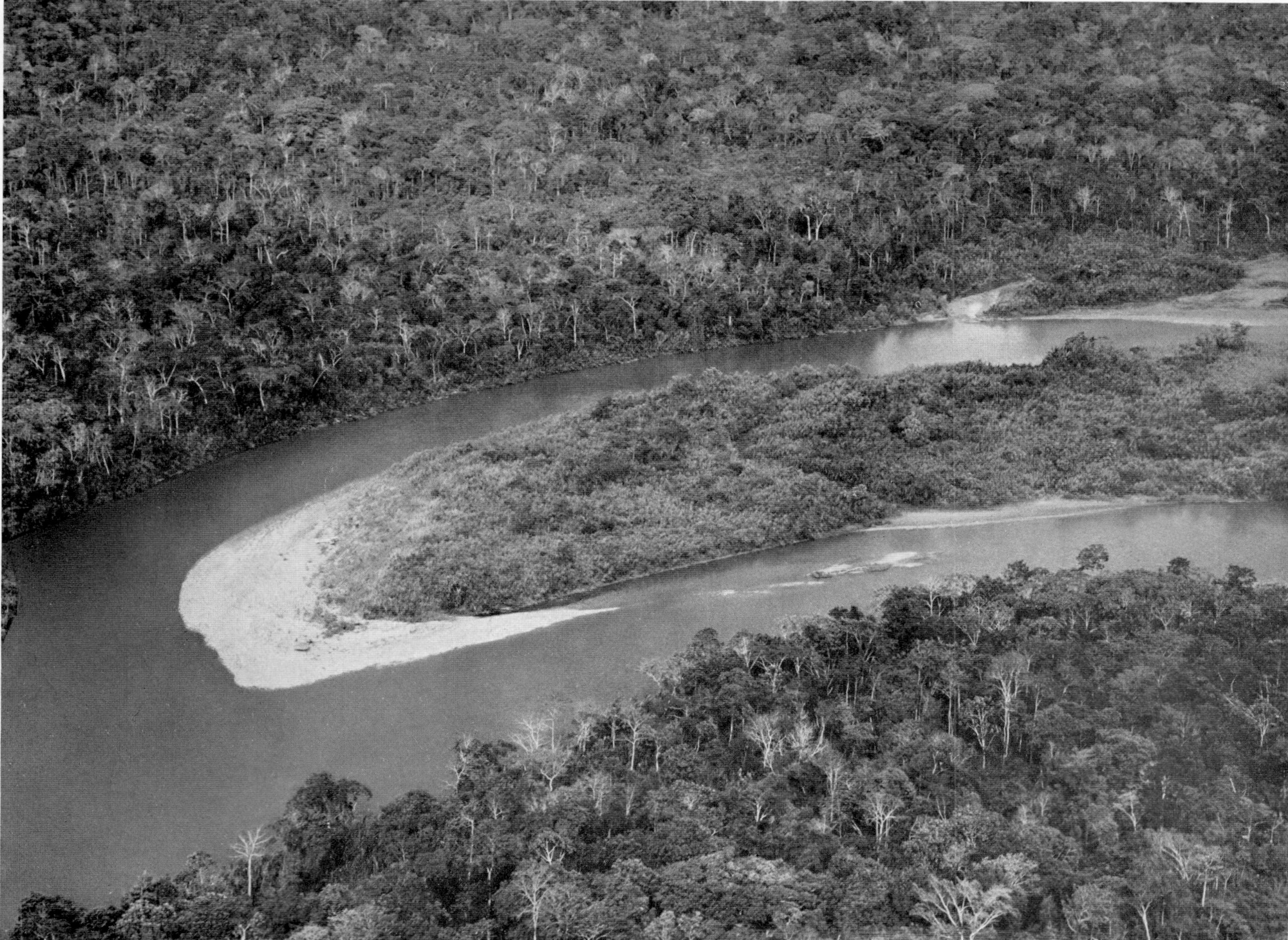

FIG. 146—A section of the Perené River. Note the dense forest and the great variety of trees as indicated by the different shades reproduced by the camera. The seaplane on the beach at the left end of the island is one of the planes of the Peruvian Naval Air Service which was forced to land there on account of engine trouble. It was while searching for this plane that Lieutenant Johnson obtained his photographs of the Perené River. Seaplanes are used in this section because the wide rivers provide convenient landing places.

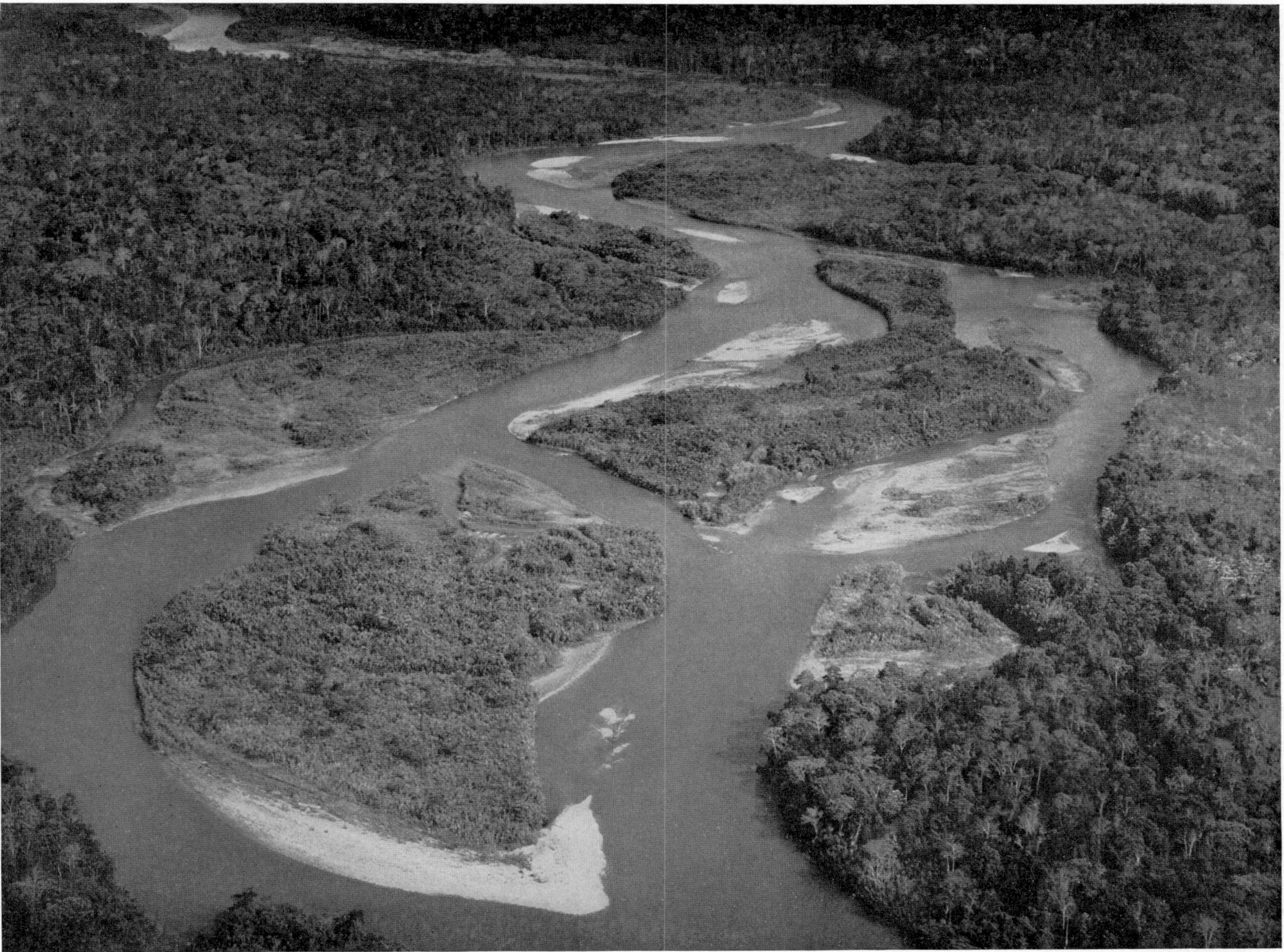

Fig. 147—Another view of the section of the Perené River shown in Figure 146. The island in the foreground with the plane on the beach is that shown in the preceding photograph. Note also the group of Indian huts at the lower right end of the island.

FIG. 148—Puerto Yessup on the Pichis River is at the head of canoe navigation on the river. On the land-and-water route from La Merced to Iquitos one can either leave the mule trail here and take canoes down to the head of launch navigation at Puerto Bermudez (see Fig. 31) or continue by muleback on down to the latter port. From Puerto Bermudez the trip by launch to Iquitos takes from twelve to fifteen days.

FIG. 149—Puerto Victoria is located at the point where the Palcazú and Pichis rivers unite to form the Pachitea River about fifty miles down stream from Puerto Yessup. The owner of the clearing is a German long resident there who has done much experimental work in the cultivation of tropical products for export and is steadily bringing new land under cultivation. Note the new clearing in the foreground.

Fig. 150—Maquina on the Pachitea River a short distance below Puerto Victoria is one of many attempts to establish colonies on the upper tributaries of the Ucayali River, most of which have ended in failure on account of the difficulty of clearing away the jungle, the constant menace of tropical diseases, and the lack of transportation. Note in the photograph the large clearings now returning to the jungle.

NOTES ON THE PHOTOGRAPHS

1. THE BIRD ISLANDS OF PERU AND THE GUANO INDUSTRY (SEE FRONTISPIECE AND FIGS. 44, 79, 101, AND 102)

The fertility of the irrigated lands of the coastal valleys of Peru is derived from two sources—the silt brought down by the rivers which water them and the easily available fertilizer obtained from the coastal islands. This fertilizer, known as guano, is composed of the droppings of the enormous flocks of birds which feed on the teeming fish life of the cold Humboldt Current (see page 9) and nest on the offshore islands. It is one of the most effective and most easily absorbed fertilizers known, the value of the best grade, calculated according to its nitrogen content, being thirty-three times that of farmyard manure.

The Incas, and probably their predecessors, knew the value of this fertilizer and it was largely due to their intelligent use of it that the Spanish conquerors found the coastal valleys in such a high state of productiveness. Under the Incas the guano supply was carefully conserved and distributed and the birds protected. After the Conquest agriculture in the coastal valleys was allowed to decline while the conquerors exploited the mineral wealth of the country and the guano deposits of the coastal islands were almost forgotten. About 1840 they were rediscovered and for more than fifty years thereafter the deposits (many of them probably the accumulations of thousands of years) were ruthlessly exploited for foreign market without consideration for the preservation of the birds or the conservation of a supply sufficient for the country's own needs. Between 1851 and 1872 it is estimated that from one small group of islands alone more than ten thousand tons were removed, representing an average annual exportation of twenty to thirty million dollars worth.

By the end of the nineteenth century not only were the deposits reduced to a point where it seemed that their exhaustion was imminent but the number of birds had been so diminished by the wanton methods of extraction employed that it seemed highly improbable that sufficient new guano could be produced to supply the country's needs.

Fortunately the government of Peru recognized the danger in time and took possession of all the deposits except those on two islands from which the Peruvian Corporation, under the contract mentioned in the legend of Figure 144, page 150, has still the right to extract several hundred thousand tons. Now the entire supply of guano, except that on the islands still operated by the Peruvian Corporation, is reserved for the use of the agricultural areas of the country, and is administered by a semi-official monopoly known as the Compañía Administradora del Guano which has full authority to enforce the laws dealing with the preservation of the birds and the conservation and distribution of the guano supply. The ships of the fleet operated by this company (see Frontispiece) visit every port of Peru carrying to the farmers of the coastal valleys the allotments of guano assigned to them according to their needs. (For a recent study of the birds of the Peruvian coast and the guano industry, see Robert Cushman Murphy: Bird Islands of Peru, New York, 1926.)

2. THE TOWN OF PISCO AND ITS PORT (SEE FIGS. 109 AND 110)

Pisco, like many of the towns of the coast of Peru, consists of two parts—the *puerto*, at a point where a headland affords some protection for shipping, the inhabitants of which are chiefly the stevedores and boatmen required for loading and unloading operations, and the *pueblo*, or main part of the town, located some distance back from the shore in the midst of the irrigated valley which the *puerto* serves. There are a number of reasons for such an arrangement. Most of the immediate coast is desert. Living conditions are unpleasant there. If there are to be gardens, however small, water must be brought in most cases several miles to irrigate them, as must also water for drinking and household purposes. Sand blown up from the beach steadily invades the streets. In times of high water a settlement on the shore is apt to be flooded. Finally, only a limited number of persons are required for the actual port operations, the majority of the inhabitants of the coastal towns being employed on the estates of the coastal valleys or in the factories, such as cotton gins. sugar mills, and rice-hulling mills, required for preparing the products of the valleys for exportation. The result has been that in a great many cases the main part of the town has been located inland, leaving only the settlement of stevedores and boatmen in the settlement at the pier.

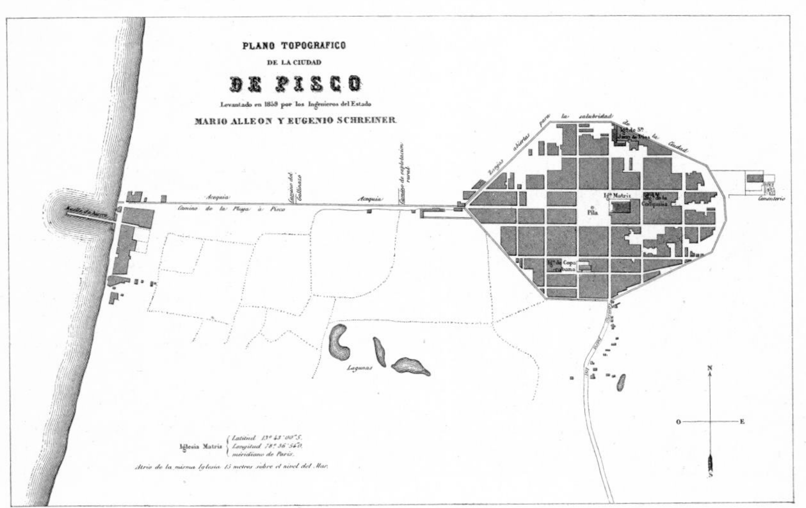

FIG. 151—An old map of the town of Pisco and its port from the Paz Soldan "Atlas Geográfico del Perú" published in 1865.

The town of Pisco was originally located on the coast, for the irrigated lands of the delta of the Pisco River come down to the sea; but, after several disastrous floods which almost completely destroyed it, the main part of the town was rebuilt in its present location. Now, however, although the *pueblo* has still the greater residential population, the business of the town has largely moved back to the *puerto*. There are now located several cotton gins and other factories including a copper smelter which uses shells from the beach for flux. The peculiar shape of the *pueblo* has remained much the same as it was originally planned in 1713. The wide roadway which encircles it was designed to permit the free circulation of air.

3. THE CAMANÁ VALLEY (SEE FIGS. 113 TO 115)

The lower Camaná Valley is potentially one of the best watered of the coastal valleys of Peru, but it has the poorest facilities for exporting its products of any of the coastal valleys and, as a result, there is much land in the valley for which a full perennial supply of water is easily available which is entirely unoccupied and much which is not under cultivation to its full production capacity.

The valley has no nearby port. The Camaná River has built a broad alluvial plain between the headlands at its mouth, and not only has the natural indentation afforded by these headlands been filled up and the river itself shoaled but the sea bottom has also been so shoaled that, if a port were to be established at the mouth of the river, ships would have to anchor far offshore. It has been suggested that the problem of a port at the mouth of the river might be solved by means of a floating dock and tower anchored out of reach of the surf and connected with the shore by means of an aerial cableway. At present the farmers of the upper valley transport their products to the Mollendo-Arequipa railway by mule-back across the high pampas back of the Coast Range, while those of the lower valley send their products by a trail along the coast to Quilca (see map, Fig. 2, page 2), whence it is transferred by small vessels to Mollendo. (For further description of the Camaná Valley, see Isaiah Bowman: The Andes of Southern Peru, American Geographical Society, 1916.)

4. EL MISTI VOLCANO (SEE FIGS. 21 AND 122 TO 128)

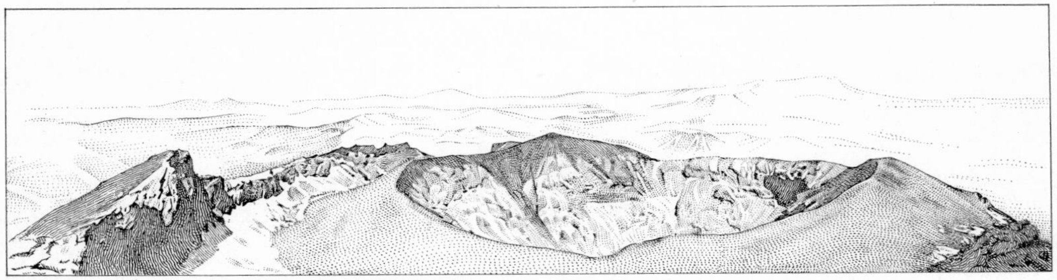

FIG. 152—A sketch of the summit of El Misti made from a photograph taken from the summit meteorological station of the Arequipa Observatory of Harvard College, looking east across the two craters of the volcano.

There has been considerable controversy as to when the first ascent of El Misti was made. Paz Soldan, the Peruvian geographer, in his "Geografía del Perú" published in 1862, expressed the opinion, without any very good reasons, that, in spite of the number of reported ascents, no white man had actually ascended to the craters. It was probably because of this statement by so eminent an authority that Dr. Isaac T. Coates, an American who made the ascent in 1873, claimed to be the first white man to reach the summit (see Lieut. H. C. Cochrane: The Misti, and Travels in Peru and Chili, *Journ. Amer. Geogr. Soc.*, Vol. VI, 1874, p. 212). There is, however, considerable evidence that a number of ascents were made before that time.

The first ascent of which there is an account is said to have been made in 1677 by a priest, Alvaro Melendez. Evidence that he actually reached the craters is to be found in the fact that his report of finding within the crater (he apparently did not see the inner crater) the stone and wood remains of a small building were verified more than two hundred years later by Juan L. de Romaña, a citizen of Arequipa who made several ascents in 1878, and by members of the staff of the Arequipa Observatory of Harvard College, who, in 1893, established a weather station on the highest point of the outer crater. Both parties reported that the stones in the form of what appeared to be the foundations of a small three-room building were still visible although the wooden remains reported by Melendez had disappeared. The stones had evidently been brought from some distance and it is believed that the building was used for religious services for the propitiation of the volcano.

The next reported ascent was made more than a century later by an expedition sent out in 1784 by Bishop Miguel Gonzalez de Pamplona to place a cross on the summit. An iron cross believed to have been erected by this expedition still stands on the highest point of the outer crater. Near it the Arequipa Observatory of Harvard College maintained a weather station for several years.

In 1891 members of the staff of the Harvard Observatory made the ascent with the object of establishing a station of self-recording meteorological instruments, and in 1893 succeeded in getting to the summit with a mule-train. Later instruments and material for the construction of the shelters were transported to the summit on mule-back and a station established on the west side of the outer crater at its highest point. The accepted altitude of the volcano (19,200 feet) was measured by triangulation by members of the staff of the Observatory. (See Annals of the Astronomical Observatory of Harvard College, Vol. XXXIX, 1899.)

AMERICAN GEOGRAPHICAL SOCIETY

SPECIAL PUBLICATION SERIES

No.		Date
1.	Memorial Volume of the Transcontinental Excursion of 1912 of the American Geographical Society of New York. [Edited by W. L. G. Joerg.] 407 pp.	1915
2.	The Andes of Southern Peru: Geographical Reconnaissance Along the Seventy-Third Meridian. By Isaiah Bowman. 336 pp.	1916
3.	The Frontiers of Language and Nationality in Europe. By Leon Dominion. 375 pp.	1917
4.	The Face of the Earth as Seen from the Air: A Study of the Application of Airplane Photography to Geography. By W. T. Lee. 110 pp.	1922
5.	Desert Trails of Atacama. By Isaiah Bowman. 360 pp.	1924
6.	China: Land of Famine. By W. H. Mallory. 119 pp.	1926
7.	Problems of Polar Research. By thirty-one authors. 477 pp.	1928
8.	The Geography of the Polar Regions. By Otto Nordenskjöld and Ludwig Mecking. 355 pp.	1928
9.	The Coral Reef Problem. By W. M. Davis. 596 pp.	1928
10.	Richard Hakluyt and the English Voyages. By G. B. Parks. 289 pp.	1928
11.	Two Polar Maps: (1) Physical Map of the Arctic, 1:20,000,000; (2) Bathymetric Map of the Antarctic, 1:20,000,000. Accompanied by "Brief History of Polar Exploration Since the Introduction of Flying." By W. L. G. Joerg. 50 pp.	1930
12.	Peru from the Air. By Lieut. George R. Johnson. 172 pp.	1930